Teacher's Guide
Yellow Level
Rose Griffiths

Heinemann Educational Publishers
Halley Court, Jordan Hill, Oxford OX2 8EJ
a division of Reed Educational & Professional Publishing Ltd

Oxford Melbourne Auckland
Florence Prague Madrid Athens
Singapore Tokyo Sao Paulo
Chicago Portsmouth NH (USA) Mexico City
Ibadan Gaborone Johannesburg
Kampala Nairobi Kuala Lumpur

First published 1997

00 99 98 97
10 9 8 7 6 5 4 3 2 1

ISBN 0 435 53335 5

Designed and typeset by Susan Clarke
Illustrated by Teri Gower and Jeff Edwards
Cover design by Ron Kamen
Printed and bound in Great Britain by Thomson Litho Ltd

The author and publishers would like to thank teachers at the
following schools for their help in trialling these materials:
Folville Junior School, Leicester
Knighton Fields Primary School, Leicester
Wolsey House Primary School, Leicester
Emmer Green Primary School, Reading
St Anne's Primary School, Streetly
Orton Wistow Primary School, Peterborough
Spooner Row Primary School, Wymondham
Stafford Leys Primary School, Leicester
St Peter's Primary School, Blaenavon

Contents

Mathematical content

Overall content for Number Connections

Red level
Counting and place value with numbers to 35
Arithmetic within 15
Mental recall of number bonds to 7

Blue level
Counting and place value with numbers to 75
Arithmetic within 40
Mental recall of number bonds to 10

Green level
Counting and place value with numbers to 120
Arithmetic within 60
Mental recall of number bonds to 15

Yellow level
Counting and place value with numbers to 200
Arithmetic within 120
Mental recall of number bonds to 20

Content of Yellow level

Yellow Textbook 1

Counting to 150
Using money
Addition and subtraction within 80
Mental recall of tables facts:
  all of the 0, 1, 2 and 10 times tables,
  and 3s, 4s and 5s within 25
Ordinal numbers (1st to 31st)
$\frac{1}{2}$s and $\frac{1}{4}$s
Multiplying 2-digit numbers by 2 or 3
  within 80

Yellow Textbook 2

Counting to 180
Using money
Addition, subtraction and
  multiplication within 100
Mental recall of tables facts: all of the
  0, 1, 2, 3, 4, 5 and 10 times tables
Multiples of 6 to 60
Dividing 2-digit numbers by 2
  within 100
Negative numbers

Yellow Textbook 3

Counting to 200
Using money
Addition and subtraction within 120
Mental recall of tables facts: all of the
  0, 1, 2, 3, 4, 5 and 10 times tables,
  and 6s within 36
Mental recall of number bonds
  within 20
Multiplying and dividing by 2, 3, 5
  and 10 within 120
$\frac{1}{2}$s, $\frac{1}{4}$s, $\frac{1}{3}$s and $\frac{1}{5}$s

Introduction

Number Connections is an exciting course providing enjoyable and well-structured materials for pupils aged 7 to 11 who have difficulty with mathematics, and in particular with number work. It can be used to support individual, small group or whole-class teaching, depending on how mathematics is organised in the school.

For each of 4 levels, Red, Blue, Green and Yellow, there are three Textbooks, associated Copymasters and a Teacher's Guide.

Stage	Pupil Books	Copymasters	Teacher's Guide
Red			
Blue			
Green			
Yellow			

Using this Teacher's Guide

This guide has been written to be used by class teachers, special needs staff, and any other adults working with the children. As well as these general introductory notes, specific notes for textbook and copymaster pages are included on pages 15 to 62. These explain the **purpose** of each section, list the **materials** needed, and suggest **supporting activities** which can be used as introductory activities before starting the textbook work, or as additional practice later on. The notes on **using the textbook pages** and **using the copymasters** include ideas about how to support children's work, information about any likely difficulties which children may have, and answers for textbook questions. *You may wish to make your own folder of one copy of each copymaster with the answers filled in with red pen.*

Using the pupil materials

The **textbooks** provide attractive, full-colour pages to work from. Children who have had difficulty with mathematics are less likely than others to have used a textbook before, and it is important not to underestimate the help that many children will need, particularly at first, to follow question numbers in the right order and to write their work down in a clear way in an exercise book. You may want to establish a routine – for example, 'title, today's date, question number 1' – so that children know what to do each time they start work. One way of showing how helpful it is to write question numbers and answers clearly, is to ask children to swap books with a friend, then mark their friend's work as you read out the answers.

T An introduction by the teacher is especially important on pages marked with the icon shown in the margin. Whatever the activity, children will often benefit from an adult reading through each page with them and discussing it, before they start work. Further notes on ways of providing **reading support** are on page 11.

For each pair of textbook pages the **copymasters** provide important additional work in a fill-in format, as well as optional extra practice. The teacher's notes for each copymaster give guidance on this. There are also copymasters with each book to make repeatable games. (See page 10 for a summary of these.) Use the copymasters as flexibly as you wish; you may want children to leave some out, or to repeat some several times. Many copymasters (including the games) provide work suitable for taking home, if wished.

Most of the copymasters are in pairs, and are associated with the same textbook spread. The copymasters can be printed back-to-back, to save paper. (The only exceptions are those which require cutting out.) It is helpful to use a variety of colours of paper if possible, to help differentiate one sheet from another. Avoid dark colours, however, as these reduce legibility.

You may wish to keep a stock of ready-printed sheets for each textbook in a concertina file or an A4 'display book' (which has clear plastic pockets), to avoid the inconvenience of too many trips to the photocopier.

The games can be made most easily if they are printed on card, and will last longer if they are laminated or covered with clear sticky-backed plastic.

Low attainment in number work

Low attainment in mathematics can be due to a great variety of reasons, including absence from school, lack of confidence, low reading ability, poor concentration and memory, and difficulties with understanding abstract ideas. Sometimes children's problems are made worse by the hierarchical nature of some parts of maths: especially with number work, children can fail because they have been moved on to a harder topic before they are sufficiently confident with the easier work on which that topic depends.

Helping children succeed

How can you best help children with number work?

Use a variety of approaches

Because of the varied nature of children's difficulties, they need a variety of teaching approaches. *Number Connections* introduces and practises each topic or skill in several contexts, and children are often encouraged to use two or three complementary methods to solve a problem, to increase their understanding of what they are doing, and to help them memorise important facts. Practical work, discussion, work with a calculator, using equipment, and pencil and paper methods, are all important. Since mental arithmetic is often the most useful method for everyday life, children need to be helped to develop a good repertoire of mental methods, too.

Capitalise on children's own interests and experience

The contexts used in these materials have been chosen both because they are interesting and relevant to children in this age group, and because they can be used to develop children's ability in using and applying maths. It is important to make the most of children's own experience, both in school and at home, so that their number work is purposeful. Many of the activities and games included can be taken home to use with parents or other family members who are keen to help the child make progress.

Use a sensible sequence of work

Each strand of work in these books is revisited several times, each time moving further forward. The sequence of topics and activities within each book (and between books) has been chosen carefully, both to make the most of links between one topic and another, and to provide variety (and hence help children to concentrate, because their interest is held).

To help you to trace the development through a particular number topic, the work is categorised into four strands: Counting and place value (in the early books, including handwriting); Addition and subtraction; Multiplication and division; and Mixed problems. See contents pages, on pages 15, 31 and 47, for work which encompasses elements from the counting and place value, addition and subtraction and multiplication and division strands.

The chart on page iv lists the mathematical content of this level of the scheme.

Encourage children to be independent and responsible

Children who have been unsuccessful at maths in the past sometimes put more effort into avoiding work or copying other people's answers than into trying to understand their work, perhaps because they have convinced themselves they will always fail. Use careful assessment (see Starting points, page 8) to decide the most appropriate starting point for a child, to help them succeed as soon as possible. Encourage them to organise themselves (even though it is often quicker for you to do it for them!) whenever possible, including fetching their own equipment when needed, and putting it away afterwards. A list of useful equipment is included below. Suggest that children work with a friend, so that they can compare answers and explain to each other how they got them.

Equipment

Very little equipment is needed other than the usual classroom stationery – pencils, ruler, scissors, glue and squared and plain paper. You will need:

- ▶ *counting equipment* for example, counters, marbles, craft sticks and any other collection of about 120 items which children would enjoy counting
- ▶ *base 10 equipment* such as Multibase or Dienes'
- ▶ *bricks* which fit together, for example, Multilink, to count singly and in groups
- ▶ *calculator* with well-spaced buttons and a display which is easy to read. It is helpful if children have the opportunity to use more than one model of calculator
- ▶ *coins and notes* – up to 80p in each coin: 1p, 2p, 5p, 10p, 20p, and some 50p and £1 coins. Real coins are better than card or plastic, and should be used at least some of the time. '£5 notes' and '£10 notes' can be made by the children.
- ▶ *stopwatch or sand timer* to time tests: 3 minutes, 2 minutes and 1 minute
- ▶ *real clock* with hands
- ▶ *number line* for desk-top or wall, marked 0–100 or more
- ▶ *dice* marked 1–6 and 0–5
- ▶ *number cards* numbered 0–70 or more
- ▶ *number tiles* showing digits 0–9
- ▶ *pack of playing cards*.

Some of the supporting activities which are suggested need other inexpensive equipment; this is listed for each activity.

Starting points

Although most children will start work on Red Textbook 1 and then work through the textbooks in order, you can start a child at any point in the scheme. It is better for a child to start on a book which can be completed quickly and successfully, and then move on, than to start on a book which proves too difficult and discourages them. If a child is new to your school or your class, use a combination of methods to decide upon the best starting point:

Previous records Compare the child's records for number work in his or her previous school or class with the list of mathematical content for each textbook on page iv.

Progress tests Ask the child to complete one version of the progress test for each textbook, starting with the easiest, and stopping as soon as the child seems to be finding a test too difficult.

The first activity in each textbook provides a check on whether the child is ready for the work in that book. Follow the advice in the teacher's notes for those pages.

Self-assessment Once a child has made a start on the work in a particular book, discuss with them whether it is at about the right level of difficulty.

Assessment, record keeping and planning

For many mathematical activities, what a child understands and can do is best assessed by observing the child and discussing their work with them. However, pencil and paper tests *are* useful as a way of reminding children about the work they have done, and to demonstrate the progress they have made. Copiable **progress tests** for each textbook are on pages 63 to 69.

Copiable **record sheets** for each textbook are included on pages 70 to 78. There are versions for the teacher and the pupil. The teacher's record covers one textbook and associated copymasters on a single sheet; the pupil's sheets cover half a textbook at a time.

There is space on both the teacher and pupil record sheets to keep notes about other activities, for example those suggested in the supporting activities in the teacher's notes for each page. This space can be used to make a note of any regular practice you would like the child to do, whilst they are working on that book – for example, writing 3 the right way round, or practising counting out money at home once a week.

Individual education plans for children with special needs, specifying each child's particular targets for work in number, are very straightforward to draw up, once you have identified which textbook in *Number Connections* is the most appropriate one for the pupil. Use the statements of mathematical content listed on the chart on page iv. (The list is also repeated at the top of the teacher's record sheet for each book.)

Curriculum coverage

See pages 79 and 80 for curriculum information for England and Wales, Scotland and Northern Ireland.

Games

Games provide useful extra practice for children who are trying to develop fluency with numbers and mental recall of number facts. It is helpful if an adult can play each new game once or twice with the child, to make sure they understand what to do; thereafter, children can use the illustrated instructions as a reminder if needed.

Most games can be played by 1, 2 or 3 people. Many children will find it helpful to practise on their own for a while, as well as playing with others.

The games included in the textbooks, and those made from copymasters, can be used as often as you wish, starting from the point where they are introduced. Extra copies of games can be lent to children to take home for additional practice with friends and family.

Textbook 1

Times tables bingo (pages 8 and 9 onwards; Y27 and Y28)
Tables facts within 25.

Calculator race (pages 18 and 19 onwards; Y29 and Y30)
Addition within 80.

Add nine (page 23)
Addition of 9 within 80.

Textbook 2

Half price sale (pages 8 and 9 onwards; Y58 and Y59)
Halving and doubling money.

Stars and dice (page 11)
Tables facts within 36.

What's missing? (pages 24 and 25 onwards; Y60, Y61 and Y62)
Missing numbers and operations.

Make one hundred (page 32)
Addition to 100.

Textbook 3

Make 200 (page 5)
Counting to 200.

Eighteens (pages 8 and 9 onwards; Y88 and Y89)
Addition bonds to 18.

Make 20 (pages 16 and 17 onwards; Y90, Y91 and Y92)
Addition and subtraction bonds within 20.

Reading support

Many children who have difficulties with number work find reading difficult as well. Teaching reading can often go hand-in-hand with teaching maths, and using non-fiction texts as well as fiction increases the opportunities to repeat important words and phrases. Children who have been relatively unsuccessful when reading stories may be more confident with the *Number Connections* books, because of the high level of repetition, the help provided by illustrations, and the activity involved.

Liaison

The approach to teaching reading which is most effective will vary from one child to another. Liaison between the child's usual teacher for maths, and their teacher for reading (if it is not the same person) is important.

Motivation

One of the most important factors in whether a child will be successful when reading a text is their motivation. Discussion before a child starts work (which will include saying out loud many of the words they will soon read) is very helpful. The contexts for number work in these books have been chosen because they are of interest to many children, and a few minutes talking with a child to make personal links with their own experience is time well spent.

Key words and phrases

Most of the vocabulary used in *Number Connections* will be familiar to children; but sometimes they will be introduced to new words and phrases which are important in maths.

These **key words and phrases** are used frequently:

how many	count	you need
draw	ask your teacher	make
write	ask your friend	use
take turns	copy and complete	fill in the missing numbers
check	add	take away
altogether	find as many ways as you can	how much change

There are photocopiable **word lists** for the Yellow textbooks on the next three pages. Each list gives up to twelve words, firstly in the order they are introduced in that book, and then in alphabetical order with an illustration for each word. All the words can be learnt in context in the textbooks or copymasters.

These are some ways of using the lists for additional practice:

▶ Give each child a copy of the word list to keep in their copymaster folder. Ask them to colour in each picture when they first come across the word in the textbook.

▶ Talk to the child about learning to read some new words over the next few weeks. Ask the child to read the list of words at the top of the page (ie without illustrations). Circle any words they already know well. Repeat this every now and then, as the child works through the textbook, and circle new words learnt. Suggest that children work with a partner if they want to, and test each other.

▶ Make a set of word cards from the list (by printing onto card if possible). Cut out each of the 12 rectangles, and write the word for each card on the back of the illustrated card. Children can practise with these by trying to read the word without the picture, then turning over to see if they are right.

Word list

Name _____

Yellow Textbook 1

shells badge first second third fourth
calendar jeans hat jumper socks gloves

badge

calendar

first

fourth

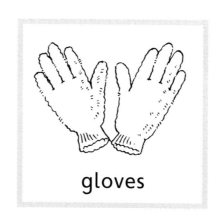

gloves

hat

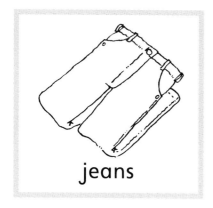

jeans

jumper

second

shells

socks

third

Number Connections © Rose Griffiths 1997
Heinemann Educational Publishers, Oxford

Word list

Yellow Textbook 2

height chart　stars　ice pop　dividing　skipping
beetle　multiplying　adding　taking away

$\begin{array}{r} 14 \\ +22 \\ \hline 36 \end{array}$ adding	 beetle	$2\overline{)3^16}\,^{18}$ dividing
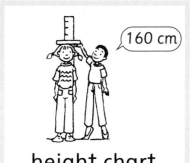 height chart	 ice pop	$\begin{array}{r} 12 \\ \times\ 3 \\ \hline 36 \end{array}$ multiplying
 skipping	☆☆ stars	$\begin{array}{r} 36 \\ -13 \\ \hline 23 \end{array}$ taking away

160 cm

Teacher's Guide

Word list

Yellow Textbook 3

doubling   halving   third   fifth   skeleton
guinea pig   penguin   fish   café   milkshake   bill

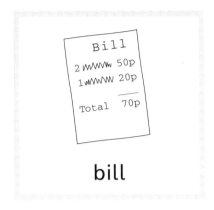

bill

café

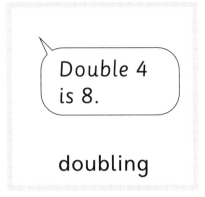

doubling

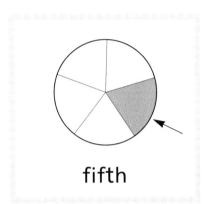

fifth

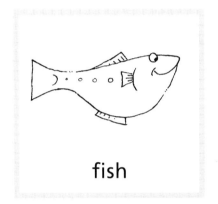

fish

guinea pig

halving

milkshake

penguin

skeleton

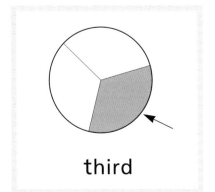

third

Number Connections © Rose Griffiths 1997
Heinemann Educational Publishers, Oxford

Yellow Textbook 1 / Copymasters Y1–Y30

Contents

Counting and place value

Addition and subtraction

Multiplication and division

Mixed problems

Textbook 1 pages 4 and 5

Seeds and shells

Textbook pages 4 and 5   Copymaster Y1

Purpose

Practising counting numbers of objects up to 150
Estimating within 150

Materials

Dessertspoon
Small quantities of small items to count, including cubes, counters, paperclips,
pennies, tags, split pins, dried peas and macaroni, if possible
Multilink (optional: for supporting activity)

Supporting activities

▶ Use Multilink or similar cubes. Count out 145 of them, one at a time. Fix as many
as you can together in lines of ten, then count them again. Which was easier:
counting in ones, or counting in tens and ones?
▶ Arrange 120 cubes in an interesting pattern in groups of 5 or 10, like the shells
on textbook page 5.

Using the textbook pages

If possible, introduce these pages by counting a dessertspoonful of sunflower
seeds, popping corn or small shells.

Most children will realise that the seeds and corn are mostly arranged in groups of
ten, and that the shells are in fives or tens; when they count the seeds, they are
likely to count '10, 20, 30, 40, 49'. If a child counts from 1 to 49 individually, it may
be an indication that they are less confident and so need further practise in
grouping in tens and counting.

Discuss the fact that the seeds and corn are smaller than the shells, so you can fit
more of them on a spoon.

(NB Any child who has difficulty counting the amounts in questions 1 to 4 should
be given further practical work, to increase their skill at counting numbers up to
150, *before* continuing with work in this book. Green Textbook 3 includes activities
and games which practise counting up to 120.)

Answers **1** 49 **2** 106 **3** 25 **4** 141

Using the copymasters

Copymaster Y1 You can only give a reasonable estimate of something if you have
previous experience of counting a similar number. The examples on the textbook
pages should give children an idea of how many of each item they may have, when
they try this themselves. Point out that an estimate is not just a random guess.

Months and years

 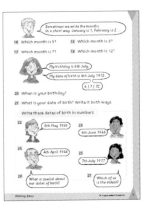  

Textbook pages 6 and 7   Copymasters Y2 and Y3

Purpose
Spelling the months of the year
Practising writing each month as a number
Ordinal numbers from 1st to 31st
Using years in order, from 1987 to 2010

Materials
Class list with birth dates (optional: for supporting activity)

Supporting activity
▶ Look at the birth dates of some of the people in your class. Which months were people born in? Were they all born in the same year?

Using the textbook pages
'Day trip' in Green Textbook 3, pages 28 and 29, looked at days of the week and began to consider days and dates. 'Days and dates' on pages 12 and 13 in this textbook takes this topic further.

January, February and August are the months which most children need to practise. Copymaster Y2 will help; children can also make up spelling puzzles for each other.

Most children will already have used 'long' and 'short' ways of writing the date, but many need to revise them. There are several acceptable short ways of writing the date, for example, 6.7.72, or 06.07.72.

Make sure children realise the numbers for each month are listed on the spelling test on textbook page 6.

Questions 20 and 21 point out the difference between your birthday (which is the same every year) and your date of birth (the date you were born).

Answers **1** to **12** Spellings of the 12 months, marked by a friend **13** to **15** Completed sequences from 1st to 31st **16** March **17** July **18** August **19** December **20** Child's own birthday **21** Child's date of birth **22** 5/5/55 **23** 6/6/66 **24** 4/4/44 **25** 7/7/77 **26** Each one uses the same numbers over and over again **27** The man in question 24, born in 1944

Using the copymasters
Copymaster Y2 Spelling practice for the months of the year. This sheet can be repeated as often as needed.

Copymaster Y3 As well as filling in the number line showing years from 1987, make sure that children can say these out loud.

Writing dates

Textbook 1 pages 8 and 9

Off by heart

Textbook pages 8 and 9

Copymasters Y4, Y27 and Y28

Purpose

Establishing or practising multiplication and division facts within 25, and improving immediate mental recall of those number facts

Materials

Calculator

Supporting activity

▶ Play 'Times tables bingo'. See Copymasters Y27 and Y28 below.

Using the textbook pages

It is worth checking that children understand what is meant by 'off by heart': that we know something so well, we no longer have to work it out. It is also important that children learn the tables facts 'all ways round': for example, they learn $2 \times 3 = 6$, $3 \times 2 = 6$, $6 \div 2 = 3$, and $6 \div 3 = 2$.

Questions 1 to 15 practise tables facts within 16. Questions 16 to 21 use the 5 times table. Questions 22 to 27 remind children that when you multiply by 0 you get 0; *no* lots of anything will be nothing. Question 30 often gets the answer 2!

Answers 1 4 **2** 12 **3** 3 **4** 8 **5** 0 **6** 2 **7** 3 **8** 4 **9** 2 **10** 0 **11** 16 **12** 4 **13** 0 **14** 2 **15** 9 **16** 15 **17** 20 **18** 2 **19** 4 **20** 10 **21** 25 **22** 0 **23** 0 **24** 0 **25** 0 **26** 0 **27** 0 **28** 0 **29** 2 **30** 1 **31** 2 **32** 4 **33** 0

Using the copymasters

Copymaster Y4 Children who feel confident with tables facts within 25 can use this sheet as a test. It can be repeated as many times as you wish.

Copymasters Y27 and Y28 'Times tables bingo'. You may wish to provide a calculator or tables square for children to check each other's answers. This game can be played as many times as you wish, from these pages onwards.

Add or take away

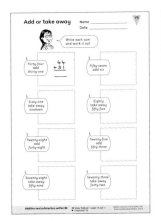
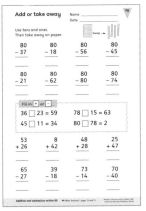

Textbook pages 10 and 11   Copymasters Y5 and Y6

Purpose

Deciding whether to add or subtract

Practising addition and subtraction within 80, using pencil and paper methods, and tens and ones equipment

Materials

Tens and ones (such as Multibase or Dienes')

Supporting activity

▶ Make up some questions like the ones on textbook pages 10 and 11 for a friend to do.

Using the textbook pages

It is important that children should be able to decide for themselves whether they need to add or subtract when solving a problem. These questions use a variety of contexts, and the language used also varies: for example, 'altogether', 'more than' and 'older than' all indicate that addition is needed. These questions also give practice in writing down sums. Some children may work out some of their answers mentally.

Answers **1** 71 **2** 47p **3** 63 **4** 54 **5** 18 **6** 27p **7** 78p **8** 71p **9** 50

Using the copymasters

Copymaster Y5 Practice at setting out sums. Some children may want to use tens and ones equipment to check their work.

Copymaster Y6 Taking away from a whole number of tens often leads to children giving an answer that is ten too big or small. Using tens and ones before using pencil and paper methods, is a great help in eliminating this common error.

Textbook 1 pages 12 and 13

Days and dates

Textbook pages 12 and 13   Copymasters Y7, Y8 and Y9

Purpose

Spelling the days of the week

Adding or multiplying sevens

Learning that a leap year has one extra day in February

Learning about the structure of a calendar

Materials

Scissors and glue (glue stick)

Calendar for this year

Other calendars, for any year (optional: for supporting activity)

Supporting activity

▶ Look at some calendars for this year or other years. Do they all have the days of the week listed in the same order? What other differences can you find? Which calendar do you find the easiest to use?

Using the textbook pages

'Months and years' on pages 6 and 7 in this textbook, revised the months, and looked at 'long' and 'short' ways of writing the date.

Check that children know that leap years are usually every 4th year. (Exceptions to this are the years at the turn of a century, *unless* the year is exactly divisible by 400. So the years 1800 and 1900 were not leap years, but the year 2000 is a leap year.) You could suggest that children try to learn the rhyme in question 18 off by heart. They can use it to fill in the chart on Copymaster Y8.

The structure of a calendar can seem very complicated to children. Questions 19 and 20 draw attention to the fact that, for example, if one month ends on a Monday, the next month must start on a Tuesday. Similarly, if one year ends on a Monday, the next year must start on a Tuesday. Children will need to use this to help them with Copymaster Y9.

Answers 1 to **7** Days of the week **8** Child's choice **9** Tuesday **10** Saturday **11** Monday **12** 7 **13** 14 **14** 21 **15** 28 **16** 35 **17** 14 **18** Copy of rhyme **19** Saturday **20** Sunday

Using the copymasters

Copymaster Y7 Helps children see how each month is listed.

Copymasters Y8 and Y9 Fitting the calendar together helps check children's understanding of the overall structure.

Speedy tables

Textbook pages 14 and 15   Copymaster Y10

Purpose

Establishing or revising multiplication and division bonds for the 0, 1, 2 and 10 times tables, and for the 3s, 4s and 5s within 25
Improving immediate mental recall of those number facts

Materials

Stopwatch or 3, 2 and 1 minute sand timers (some children may have digital watches with timers on them)
Calculator

Supporting activity

▶ Play 'Times tables bingo' made from Copymasters Y27 and Y28.

Using the textbook pages

These pages introduce a series of tables tests, following the same pattern as the timed tests used in the Blue and Green Level textbooks to improve mental recall of addition and subtraction facts. Questions 1 to 20 should be read to the child who is answering them, to help them improve their ability to take in and remember questions without seeing them in print. Some children find it very difficult to listen and concentrate; it can help them if their partner stops after questions 7 and 14, to mark them before going on. Marking sums with a calculator helps children remember any they got wrong; it also reminds them that it is quicker to do smaller sums in your head than on a calculator.

Answers **1** 2 **2** 15 **3** 12 **4** 70 **5** 20 **6** 1 **7** 9 **8** 9 **9** 1 **10** 5 **11** 4 **12** 7 **13** 4 **14** 4 **15** 25 **16** 3 **17** 6 **18** 3 **19** 0 **20** 9 **21** 8 **22** 3 **23** 2 **24** 3 **25** 2 **26** 4 **27** 5 **28** 1 **29** 5 **30** 4 **31** 4 **32** 7 **33** 10 **34** 9 **35** 0

Using the copymaster

Copymaster Y10 This provides two parallel tests covering all the significant tables facts as listed. Children should fill in their name and the date first, and *then* time the test. The timing can be done by the teacher; alternatively, two children can take turns in timing each other.

At first, allow children 3 minutes to do as much as they can (and ring the 3 in the top left-hand corner of the test sheet). Repeating the tests, a few days apart, is a good way of helping children learn these off by heart, and their scores usually improve quite quickly. When a child has scored 20 on a test, reduce the time when they next try it to 2 minutes, then finally, if wished, to 1 minute. Children should always be trying to beat *their own* previous score, or time – not to beat another child. The latter can encourage cheating, and so is not as effective.

Mental recall of tables facts

Squares

   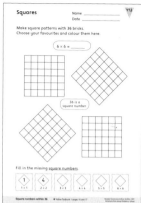

Textbook pages 16 and 17　　　　　Copymasters Y11 and Y12

Purpose

Recognising which numbers are square numbers, and which are not
Practising the tables facts 1×1, 2×2, 3×3, 4×4, 5×5 and 6×6

Materials

Multilink or other coloured bricks
Calculator

Supporting activity

▶ Use 9 bricks. How many different patterned squares can you make, if you are only allowed to use two colours?

Using the textbook pages

Check before they start work on these pages that children know a square must have sides the same length as each other. It helps children to copy the arrangements of bricks shown.

Children's understanding of square numbers is best developed by investigating numbers which are square, and numbers which are not square.

Questions 6 to 14 help children remember that 16 is a square number, by concentrating on the four by four square. They also emphasise addition facts within 16.

Answers **1** 9 **2** 9 **3** 16 **4** 16 **5** No **6** 8 **7** 8 **8** 16 **9** 12 **10** 4 **11** 16 **12** 6 **13** 10 **14** 16 **15** Yes **16** No **17** Yes

Using the copymasters

Copymaster Y11　This reviews the square numbers within 36, and concentrates on 25.

Copymaster Y12　Concentrates on 36.

Ways of adding

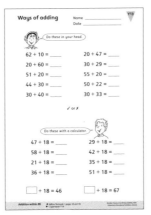
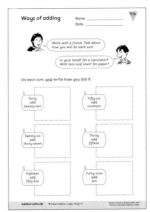

Textbook pages 18 and 19   *Copymasters Y13, Y14, Y29 and Y30*

Purpose

Practising addition within 80
Thinking about and discussing different ways of adding
Choosing appropriate methods to do different additions

Materials

Tens and ones (such as Multibase or Dienes')
Calculator
Number line 0 to 80 or more (optional)

Supporting activity

▶ Play the 'Calculator race' game. See Copymasters Y29 and Y30 below.

Using the textbook pages

In Green Textbook 3, 'In your head' on pages 30 and 31, children were encouraged to explain how they had worked things out in their heads, and to think about why they found some sums easier than others. These pages provide a chance to talk about several methods of addition, and the advantages of each one.

It is not always easy to explain why you have chosen a particular method to work something out, and it is useful to listen to other people's explanations (including the teacher's).

Answers **1** 20 **2** 39 **3** 12 **4** 66 **5** 61 **6** 15 **7** 16 **8** 50 **9** 60 **10** 32 **11** 29 **12** 70 **13** 79 **14** 65 **15** 57 **16** 80 **17** 72 **18** 67 **19** 34 **20** 77 **21** 76 **22** 76 **23** 53 **24** 80 **25** 47 **26** 67 **27** 71 **28** 68 **29** 65 **30** 76 **31** 77 **32** 74 **33** 77 **34** 68 **35** 70 **36** 69 **37** 74 **38** 69 **39** 64 **40** 70 **41** 55 **42** 38 **43** 61 **44** 82 **45** 78 **46** 76 **47** 63 **48** 52 **49** 55 **50** 75

Using the copymasters

Copymaster Y13 Further practice using mental arithmetic and a calculator. Encourage children to use their answers to the calculator sums to help them work out the missing numbers.

Copymaster Y14 Practice at setting out sums, and deciding on an appropriate method.

Copymasters Y29 and Y30 'Calculator race' game. This game aims to help children think about which sums can be done more quickly in your head than on a calculator. It can be played as many times as you like from these pages onwards.

Addition within 80

Textbook 1 pages 20 and 21

Times 2, times 3

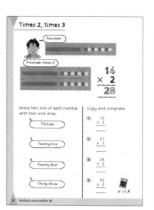 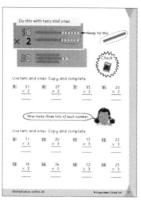

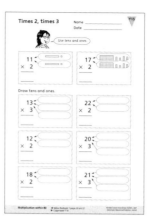 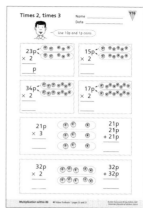

Textbook pages 20 and 21   Copymasters Y15 and Y16

Purpose

Using tens and ones equipment, to multiply 2-digit numbers by 2 or 3
Beginning to use a pencil and paper method of recording 2-digit by 1-digit multiplication

Materials

Tens and ones (such as Multibase or Dienes')
Calculator
Thirty 1p and six 10p coins (optional)

Supporting activity

▶ Make up some more sums like the ones on Copymaster Y16 for a friend to do.

Using the textbook pages

In the Green Level textbooks, children were shown how to do 2-digit additions and subtractions using tens and ones equipment; they practised with the equipment, *then* were shown the matching pencil and paper methods at a later stage. These pages begin the same process with multiplication of numbers within 80.

It is important that children *do* use tens and ones to make the numbers alongside questions 1 to 4, even if they are feeling very confident, as the tens and ones help them to build a mental picture of what is happening.

Questions 1 to 8 use multiplication by 2, and questions 9 to 16 use multiplication by 3. From question 5 onwards, some of the questions require exchanging ten ones for a ten.

'More multiplying', on textbook pages 24 and 25, take this work a step further, by showing a standard pencil and paper method of multiplying.

Answers **1** 26 **2** 42 **3** 48 **4** 66 **5** 62 **6** 54 **7** 70 **8** 40 **9** 33 **10** 60 **11** 45 **12** 66 **13** 48 **14** 72 **15** 36 **16** 75

Using the copymasters

Copymaster Y15 Drawing tens and ones to do a sum is a useful alternative to using the equipment, and helps many children move a step closer to being able to visualise the sum in their head.

Copymaster Y16 The 10p and 1p coins provide an alternative context to the Dienes' or Multibase tens and ones equipment.

Textbook 1 pages 22 and 23

Adding nine

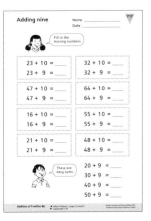
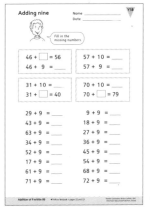

Textbook pages 22 and 23   Copymasters Y17 and Y18

Purpose

Establishing and practising a mental method of adding 9

Materials

Tens and ones (such as Multibase or Dienes')
Number line (optional: if possible, made from Green Copymaster G72)
Cards numbered 1 to 70
Calculator

Supporting activity

▶ Work with a friend. Put tens and ones on a number line made from Copymaster G72, to make any number up to 60. Ask your friend to take away nine. Check with a calculator.

Using the textbook pages

It is helpful to start by using a number line (either with tens and ones, or with a counter or a marker pen) to show that adding ten and taking one away, gets you to the same place as adding nine.

Questions 1 to 10 practise adding ten, then 'going back one' so you have added nine.

The 'Add nine' game on textbook page 23 provides useful additional practice. It helps children to play the game with an adult the first time, but it can be played as many times as you wish from then onwards.

Answers **1** 10 **2** 9 **3** 25 **4** 24 **5** 37 **6** 36 **7** 46 **8** 45 **9** 75 **10** 74

Using the copymasters

Copymaster Y17 Further practice in pairs of sums, adding ten or nine, then some examples where adding nine is very easy.

Copymaster Y18 Missing numbers problems, following the same pattern, and then further practice at adding nine.

Addition of 9 within 80   **25**

Textbook 1 pages 24 and 25

More multiplying

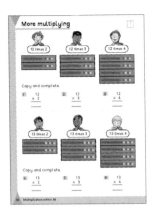

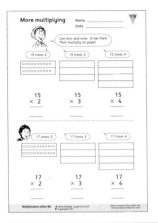

Textbook pages 24 and 25   Copymasters Y19 and Y20

Purpose

Using tens and ones equipment, to multiply 2-digit numbers by 2, 3 or 4
Introducing and practising one method of pencil and paper multiplication, showing how it links with using equipment

Materials

Tens and ones (such as Multibase or Dienes')
Calculator

Supporting activity

▶ Make up 5 more sums like those on textbook page 25 for a friend to do. Check them with a calculator.

Using the textbook pages

Earlier in this textbook, in 'Times 2, times 3' on pages 20 and 21, children used tens and ones equipment to multiply by 2 or 3 within 80, and wrote the questions in a vertical layout. In some questions they needed to exchange ten ones for a ten, but it was not always necessary.

These pages remind children of the link between multiplication and repeated addition, using tens and ones, and provide the teacher with the opportunity to show a standard pencil and paper method, including 'carrying'. It is important that children know that there are several effective ways of finding the answer to any sum; the method explained on page 25 is very useful, but it is not the only way of doing these.

Questions 7 to 10 do not all require 'carrying'. Make sure children use equipment for each one before they write anything down, and show them that when they have exchanged ten ones for a ten, they can show this on paper by writing a small 1 underneath the bottom line, below the tens figures. The most important thing is that they realise they are keeping track of *ten*, not one.

Answers **1** 24 **2** 36 **3** 48 **4** 26 **5** 39 **6** 52 **7** 72 **8** 66 **9** 69 **10** 88 **11** 34 **12** 54 **13** 64 **14** 36

Using the copymasters

Copymasters Y19 and Y20 Further practice using tens and ones, pencil and paper, and a calculator.

Shopping

Textbook pages 26 and 27   Copymasters Y21 and Y22

Purpose

Using notes and coins to add and give change within £20

Revising writing amounts of money using £ and a decimal point, or p

Materials

Coins (about £10 in total, mixed denominations) and notes (two £10 and four £5 notes, which can be made by the children)

Toy or clothes catalogue (optional: for supporting activity)

Supporting activity

▶ Work with a friend. You have £20 to spend; choose something you could buy from a catalogue. Your friend has to work out how much money you would have left.

Using the textbook pages

These pages follow a similar pattern to 'Games', in Green Textbook 3, pages 10 and 11, which looked at number bonds to 15, using whole pounds. Here the emphasis is on making amounts in pounds and pence with coins and notes, and working out change.

Most children will work out the change using the same method many adults prefer – 'counting on' – rather than calculating it by subtraction. Some children may need you to show them how to do this, making up each amount to the next number of whole pounds, then seeing how many more pounds you need.

Questions 1 and 2 give you the opportunity to check that children have remembered to write, for example, '£7.01' not '£7.1', for mixed amounts of pounds and pence where there are less than ten pence.

Check handwriting of £ signs, and if needed, use Copymasters R76 and R77, which go with pages 18 and 19 in Red Textbook 3, 'Pounds', for revision.

Answers **1** £7.01 **2** £1.05 **3** £2.25 **4** £3.01 **5** £3.50 **6** £12.50 **7** £2.50 **8** £14.00 **9** £6.00 **10** £17.50 **11** £2.50 **12** £20.00 **13** None

Using the copymasters

Copymaster Y21 Further practice at adding using coins and notes.

Copymaster Y22 Questions to make up for a friend to answer. Most children will continue to work within £20, but some may wish to be more ambitious. This sheet can be repeated as often as wished.

Lunch

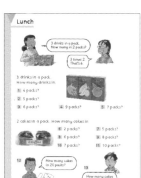

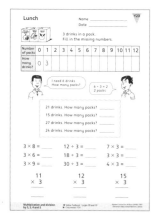

Textbook pages 28 and 29   *Copymasters Y23 and Y24*

Purpose

Practising and using the 2, 3, 4 and 5 times tables

Completing and using charts

Materials

An example of something sold in packs of 2, 3, 4 or 5 (optional: for supporting activity)

Supporting activity

▶ Find something else which is sold in packs of 2, 3, 4 or 5. Make up some questions for a friend like the ones on textbook pages 28 and 29.

Using the textbook pages

Children are more likely to remember their tables facts if they have frequent opportunities to use them in relevant contexts. These pages extend the work started in Green Textbook 3, 'Pens in packs', on pages 26 and 27.

Children who need additional support for any of the questions may find it helpful to draw all the packs and count to find the total.

Questions 12, 13, 21, 28 and 29 can be done using the pencil and paper method shown in 'More multiplying' on textbook pages 24 and 25; alternatively, children may prefer to use a method of their own.

Answers **1** 12 **2** 15 **3** 18 **4** 27 **5** 21 **6** 4 **7** 10 **8** 12 **9** 16 **10** 14 **11** 20 **12** 40 **13** 50 **14** 12 **15** 16 **16** 24 **17** 28 **18** 40 **19** 36 **20** 32 **21** 60 **22** 10 **23** 20 **24** 25 **25** 35 **26** 50 **27** 45 **28** 60 **29** 75

Using the copymasters

Copymaster Y23 Practise in multiplying and dividing by 3, including filling in a chart.

Copymaster Y24 Multiplying and dividing by 4, including filling in a chart.

Textbook 1 pages 30 and 31

Quarter each

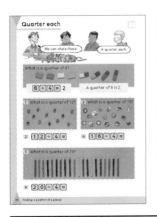  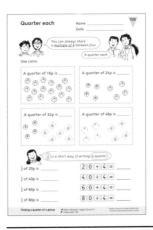 

Textbook pages 30 and 31   *Copymasters Y25 and Y26*

Purpose

Finding a quarter of a group within 80, using equipment

Finding a quarter by dividing by 4 on a calculator

Looking at contexts where we use remainders, and where we use quarters

Seeing that a quarter can be written '$\frac{1}{4}$'

Materials

Calculator

Tens and ones (such as Multibase or Dienes')

Coins (approximately £1 altogether, in 1p, 2p, 5p, and 10p coins)

Supporting activity

▶ Work with a friend. Put a pile of coins on the table. Take turns to take a handful, count how much money you have, and work out what a quarter of it is. Does it always work exactly?

Using the textbook pages

These pages follow a similar pattern to those introducing halving, in Green Textbooks 1 and 2. 'Quarter hours', on pages 22 and 23 of Green Textbook 3, used quarters in an everyday context, as parts of a whole hour. Here, the different activity of finding part of a group is developed, including the important point that dividing by four does not always work exactly. Sometimes we use fractions to solve this (for example, by cutting up an apple – so one quarter of 5 apples is $1\frac{1}{4}$) but sometimes we will have one or more items left over (for example, when finding a quarter of 5 pencil cases).

Check that children know they should write 1 and 4 much smaller than usual when they are writing $\frac{1}{4}$.

Yellow Textbook 3 revises quarters again, in 'Cheesecakes' on pages 18 and 19.

Answers **1** 3 **2** 3 **3** 4 **4** 4 **5** 5 **6** 5 **7** 1 **8** 1 **9** Not exactly. 1, remainder 1 **10** Yes. $1\frac{1}{4}$

Using the copymasters

Copymaster Y25 Using coins to give a quarter of an amount to each of 4 children. All the amounts work without remainders.

Copymaster Y26 Using tens and ones to see that you can find a quarter by halving and halving again. All the amounts work without remainders.

Textbook 1 page 32

Make forty

Textbook page 32

Purpose

Investigating ways of using addition, subtraction, multiplication and division to make 40

Checking work

Materials

Tens and ones (such as Multibase or Dienes')

Number line to 60 or more

Calculator

Using the textbook page

Previous textbooks have included similar investigations to this one, using smaller numbers and a more limited range of operations. For example, Blue Textbook 3 page 32, 'Make a dozen', looked at ways of making 12 using add, take away or multiply.

The examples shown here do not include a division; many children will only be able to think of one example: $80 \div 2 = 40$. Remind children if needed about how to write the division sign, or point it out on a calculator.

Most children will approach this in a fairly random manner, but they should be encouraged to check that they have not repeated a way of making 40 as they go along. They may wish to work with a partner.

There are an infinite number of ways of making 40, so you may want to suggest a time limit – or leave it to the child to decide when to stop.

Children can use a calculator both to try out possible sums, and to check ones they have already written down.

Yellow Textbook 2 / Copymasters Y31–Y62

Contents

▨ Counting and place value

■ Addition and subtraction

● Multiplication and division

○ Mixed problems

Textbook 2 pages 4 and 5

One hundred and eighty

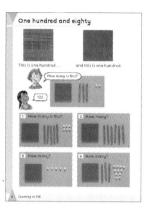

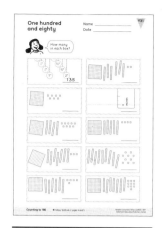

Textbook pages 4 and 5　　　　　*Copymaster Y31*

Purpose
Practising counting numbers of objects, up to 180
Checking ability to write numbers with figures (particularly 100 to 180)
Estimating within 180

Materials
Hundred, tens and ones (such as Multibase or Dienes')
180 miscellaneous small objects (optional: for supporting activity)

Supporting activity
▶ Collect between 150 and 180 small items – for example, cubes, counters, pencils and rubbers, and write that number down. Ask someone who does not know, to guess how many there are altogether. Did they get it right? Count the things again together, putting them in groups of 10 and 100 to help you to check.

Using the textbook pages
Introduce these pages by looking at the ones, tens and hundreds from structured counting equipment, to make sure children are confident that ten tens make one hundred, *and* that one hundred ones make one hundred. If a child gets question 3 wrong, check the way they write the numbers from 101 to 109.

Question 4 puzzles some children because there are more than ten ones. Questions like this are important – they check the child's ability to count 'across the tens': for example, '139, 140, 141, ...'. If a child needs further practice, use the game in Green Textbook 3, page 5, 'Who has most?', but using 12 tens and 60 ones.

Drawing each number as one hundred, tens and ones provides a written record of the child's practical activity, and provides children with a mental picture of each number, which can help develop methods for mental arithmetic.

(NB Any child who has difficulty counting the amounts in questions 1 to 4 should be given further practical work, to increase their skill at counting numbers up to 180, *before* continuing with work in this book. Yellow Textbook 1 includes activities to practise counting up to 150.)

Answers **1** 156 **2** 160 **3** 105 **4** 141 **5** to **18** Child's drawings of each number. NB Some children may use more than ten tens, or more than ten ones, to make a number. As long as the total is correct, this is permissible, but check they know that the simplest way is to use one hundred, and tens, wherever possible.

Using the copymaster
Copymaster Y31 Further practice at counting and writing numbers.

How tall are you?

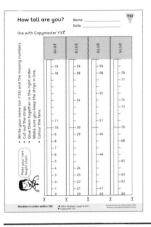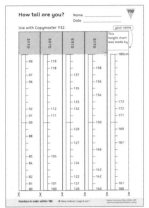

Textbook pages 6 and 7　　　　　　　*Copymasters Y32 and Y33*

Purpose

Making and using a number line (a height chart) within 180
Checking handwriting

Materials

Scissors and glue (glue stick)
Something to fix height chart to the wall

Supporting activity

► Look at 5 children in your class. Write their names in order of height, starting with the one you think is tallest. Then measure them with your height chart, to see if you were right about the order.

Using the textbook pages

Rulers and measuring tapes can often be used as number lines. Making their own height chart provides children with a useful context for writing numbers in order, and also gives an opportunity to revise and develop measuring skills. Remind children, if needed, that 'cm' is the short way of writing 'centimetres'.

Check children's handwriting as they make their charts. If needed, the handwriting chart in Red Textbook 2, made from Copymaster R34, can be used for revision.

Fixing a height chart to the wall is not a trivial task; children need to understand that it must be fixed 'straight', i.e. at right angles to the floor, with the zero mark touching the floor. Measuring yourself is not very practical, so children will need to work together! Show children how to use a book or board held on the top of someone's head to read their height off the chart.

Questions 3 to 6 could be done by addition and subtraction, or by counting forwards and backwards, either mentally or using the height measure. Children may want to make up further similar questions of their own.

Answers **1** Child's height **2** Friend's height **3** 144 cm **4** 149 cm **5** 156 cm **6** 154 cm **7** and **8** Child's specific answers

Using the copymasters

Copymasters Y32 and Y33 These two sheets together make a height chart which will be sufficient to measure people up to 180 cm tall. Remind children to write reasonably small and neatly; look at the photograph on textbook page 6 to see how to colour in alternate tens on the chart, to make it easier to read. Ask children to check each other's charts, before and after they are glued, to make sure they have got the strips in the right order.

Numbers in order within 180

Textbook 2 pages 8 and 9

Half price sale

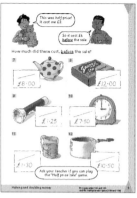

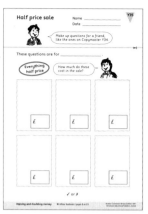

Textbook pages 8 and 9   *Copymasters Y34, Y35, Y58 and Y59*

Purpose

Revising writing amounts of money using £ and a decimal point, or p

Practising halving and doubling amounts of money

Using notes and coins to pay and give change

Materials

Coins (about £10 in total, mixed denominations) and notes (two £10 and four £5 notes, which can be made by the children)

Calculator

Supporting activity

▶ Play the 'Half price sale' game. See Copymasters Y58 and Y59 below.

Using the textbook pages

Halving and doubling was last practised in Green Textbook 3, in 'Twins' on pages 20 and 21, and in 'Diamond doubles' on page 32. These pages extend the context to using money in pounds and pence.

Questions 1 to 6 can be done mentally or using coins and notes. Children may develop different mental methods for money problems than those they used for more abstract number work; it is very common to halve money by halving the pounds, halving the pence, then adding the two together. Encourage children to discuss the methods used for each question. Questions 7 to 12 are doubling problems. Children are more likely to use pencil and paper to do these than for halving, but may still prefer to do them mentally or with coins and notes.

Check handwriting of £ signs, and if needed, use Copymasters R76 and R77, which go with pages 18 and 19 in Red Textbook 3, 'Pounds', for revision.

Answers **1** £6.00 (£6) **2** £4.50 **3** £12.50 **4** £3.25 **5** £5.50 **6** 75p **7** £16.00 (£16) **8** £24.00 (£24) **9** £2.50 **10** £15.00 (£15) **11** £2.60 **12** £21.00 (£21)

Using the copymasters

Copymaster Y34 Further practice, using coins and notes if wished.

Copymaster Y35 Questions to make up for a friend to answer. If children have set prices using odd numbers of pence, they need to decide what to do when they halve the price, since it will not work exactly. Use notes and coins to help them think about this. This sheet can be repeated as often as wished.

Copymasters Y58 and Y59 The 'Half price sale' game can be played as many times as you wish. Children could make additional cards.

Tables stars

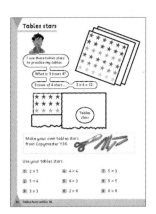

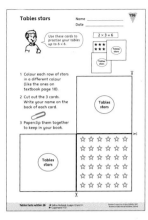
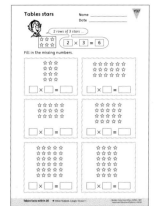

Textbook pages 10 and 11   *Copymasters Y36 and Y37*

Purpose

Establishing or practising multiplication facts within 36, and improving immediate mental recall of those number facts

Materials

Scissors and colouring pencils
Paperclip
Two 1 to 6 dice

Supporting activity

▶ Play 'Times tables bingo', made from Copymasters Y27 and Y28 from Yellow Textbook 1, to practise up to 5×5.

Using the textbook pages

Tables facts were practised in Yellow Textbook 1 in several places, including on pages 28 and 29, 'Lunch'. The tables star cards provide another way of thinking about each fact, and give children a practical and active way of practising and memorising facts to $6 \times 6 = 36$.

The star card can be turned in any direction, and you can show children that, for example, 3×5 will give you the same answer as 5×3.

The 'Stars and dice' game on page 11 can be played as many times as you wish from here onwards.

Division facts are practised later, in 'More tables stars' on pages 14 and 15.

Answers **1** 10 **2** 20 **3** 9 **4** 16 **5** 18 **6** 12 **7** 15 **8** 25 **9** 36

Using the copymasters

Copymaster Y36 Cut out to make a set of tables stars.

Copymaster Y37 This sheet checks that children understand how to write the multiplication sum which tells you how many stars are in each group. Either possibility is correct – for example $4 \times 3 = 12$, or $3 \times 4 = 12$.

Ice pops

 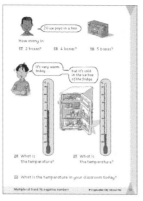  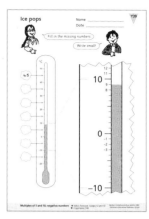

Textbook pages 12 and 13 | Copymasters Y38, Y39 and Y40

Purpose

Using the 5 and 10 times tables

Using pounds and pence

Reading and representing positive and negative temperatures on a simple thermometer

Materials

Thermometer (like the one illustrated on textbook page 13, if possible)

Coins (optional)

Supporting activity

▶ Use a thermometer to find out the temperature in your classroom at 3 or 4 times during the day. Was it always the same temperature?

Using the textbook pages

Start by talking about how much ice pops cost in shops near you.

Children can answer questions 1 to 4, and 9 to 11, very easily, if they know their 5 and 10 times table facts. They may use a variety of methods for other questions.

Questions 12 and 14 are the only two where the vertical method of multiplication is likely to be helpful (practised in Yellow Textbook 1, 'More multiplying' on pages 24 and 25). Encourage children to choose their own method, and to explain to each other how they calculated each sum. Check they remember to turn amounts of money over 100 pence into pounds and pence. Use coins to help, if needed.

Questions 15 and 16 can be answered by 'trial and improvement' instead of division, i.e. children have a guess, work out the cost, then make their 'guess' bigger or smaller until they find the right number.

Negative numbers are revised or introduced on page 13 in the context of temperatures. Most children will already know that temperature is usually measured in 'degrees Celsius', and that the short way of writing this is °C.

Answers **1** 30p **2** 50p **3** 90p **4** £1 **5** £1.20 **6** £1.50 **7** £1.70 **8** £2 **9** 25p **10** 35p **11** 40p **12** 55p **13** 45p **14** 70p **15** 6 **16** 20 **17** 40 **18** 80 **19** 100 **20** 20 degrees Celsius **21** Minus 10 degrees Celsius **22** Classroom temperature

Using the copymasters

Copymaster Y38 Showing temperatures in multiples of 5 degrees.

Copymaster Y39 Looking at the scale, 1 degree at a time, from +10° C to −10° C.

Copymaster Y40 Further practice at reading the scale on a thermometer.

Textbook 2 pages 14 and 15

More tables stars

Textbook pages 14 and 15   Copymasters Y41 and Y42

Purpose

Establishing and practising multiplication and division facts within 36

Improving immediate mental recall of those number facts

Introducing another method of writing a division (e.g. $3\overline{)15}$)

Materials

Tables stars made from Copymaster Y36

Two 1 to 6 dice (optional: for supporting activity)

Calculator

Supporting activity

▶ Play the 'Stars and dice' game on textbook page 11.

Using the textbook pages

The tables stars were introduced on pages 10 and 11, and used to practise multiplication facts up to $6 \times 6 = 36$. These pages use the stars to revise the complementary division facts.

It is important that children recognise a variety of ways of talking about a division question, so that they know, for example, that we can say 'What is 15 divided by 3?' or 'How many 3s make 15?' and that both questions have the answer '5'. They should also realise that 5 is the missing number in the multiplication $3 \times ? = 15$.

The example illustrated on page 14 shows the tables stars being used to find the answer to $15 \div 3$ by trial and improvement, counting up successive rows of 3 until it makes 15.

Page 15 introduces (or revises, for some children) an alternative way of writing a division. It is actually a less convenient way if you are using a calculator, or if you know the division facts off by heart, but it is an important method to know about, for when you want to divide larger numbers. Later in this book, 'Dividing marbles' on pages 26 and 27 will take this method further.

Answers **1** 4 **2** 6 **3** 3 **4** 5 **5** 4 **6** 5 **7** 3 **8** 6 **9** 3 **10** 4 **11** 3 **12** 6 **13** 4 **14** 6 **15** 6 **16** 5 **17** 5 **18** 5 **19** 6 **20** 6 **21** 4

Using the copymasters

Copymaster Y41 Further divisions, represented with stars.

Copymaster Y42 Using the two main ways of writing a division alongside each other; children should use mental recall, or their stars cards, then the calculator, for each one.

Tables facts within 36

Speedy tables

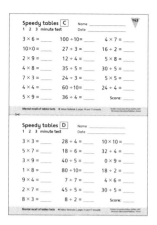

Textbook pages 16 and 17 — Copymaster Y43

Purpose

Establishing or revising multiplication and division bonds for the 0, 1, 2, 3, 4, 5 and 10 times tables

Improving immediate mental recall of those number facts

Materials

Stopwatch or 3, 2 and 1 minute sand timers (some children may have digital watches with timers on them)

Calculator

Supporting activity

▶ Play the 'Stars and dice' game on textbook page 11.

Using the textbook pages

These pages continue a series of timed tables tests introduced in Yellow Textbook 1, to improve mental recall of tables facts. Questions 1 to 20 should be read to the child who is answering them, to help them improve their ability to take in and remember questions without seeing them in print. Some children find it very difficult to listen and concentrate; it can help them if their partner stops after questions 7 and 14, to mark them before going on. Marking sums with a calculator helps children remember any they got wrong; it also reminds them that it is quicker to do these smaller sums in your head than on a calculator.

Answers **1** 12 **2** 14 **3** 0 **4** 8 **5** 60 **6** 20 **7** 12 **8** 4 **9** 8 **10** 5 **11** 7 **12** 8 **13** 10 **14** 6 **15** 24 **16** 9 **17** 40 **18** 9 **19** 36 **20** 5 **21** 5 **22** 4 **23** 6 **24** 7 **25** 4 **26** 1 **27** 6 **28** 7 **29** 8 **30** 4 **31** 3 **32** 1 **33** 3 **34** 10 **35** 10

Using the copymaster

Copymaster Y43 This provides two parallel tests covering all the significant tables facts as listed. Children should fill in their name and the date first, and then time the test. The timing can be done by the teacher; alternatively, two children can take it in turns to time each other.

At first, allow children 3 minutes to do as much as they can (and ring the 3 in the top left-hand corner of the test sheet). Repeating the tests, a few days apart, is a very effective way of helping children learn these off by heart, and their scores ususaly improve quite quickly. When a child has scored 20 on a test, reduce the time when they next try it to 2 minutes, then finally, if wished, to 1 minute. Children should always be trying to beat *their own* previous score or time, not to beat another child. The latter can encourage cheating, and so is not as effective.

Keeping fit

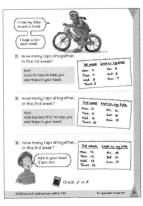
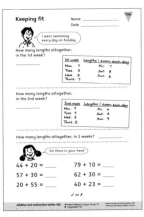

Textbook pages 18 and 19   Copymasters Y44 and Y45

Purpose

Practising addition and subtraction within 100, using pencil and paper methods, tens and ones equipment, mental arithmetic, and a calculator

Revise spellings of days of the week

Materials

Tens and ones (such as Multibase or Dienes')

Calculator

Supporting activity

▶ Keep a chart for a week of something you can count – for example, can you do 50 sums each day? Make up sums for yourself, or swap with a friend. How many did you do in a whole week?

Using the textbook pages

The problems given here can be worked out in a great variety of ways. Some children will use mental methods, others will prefer to use pencil and paper, or tens and ones equipment. When adding in their heads, the questions on page 19 include hints to help with these particular examples. Looking for tens (5 + 5, 6 + 4) has been practised before, and is revised in question 7. Question 8 is easy to add by counting up tens first, to get 70, then adding on 1, 2 and 4, to make 77. Encourage children to discuss the methods they use; many children find it helpful to use tens and ones to explain their mental methods. Remind them, too, that it is sensible to check your adding by adding up again in a different order.

Question 6 revises the spellings of the three days which most children find most difficult!

Answers **1** 91 **2** 9 **3** 95 **4** 5 **5** Copy of chart with daily totals filled in: 93, 100, 100, 96, 90, 100, 90 **6** Tuesday, Wednesday, Saturday **7** 37 **8** 77 **9** 89

Using the copymasters

Copymaster Y44 Further practice in a similar context.

Copymaster Y45 Further practice using tens and ones alongside pencil and paper addition.

Textbook 2 pages 20 and 21

Six times table

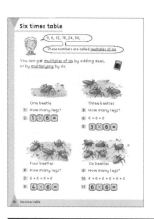
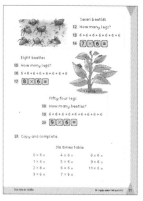
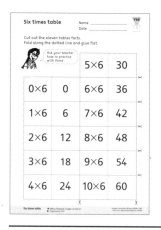

Textbook pages 20 and 21   Copymasters Y46 and Y47

Purpose

Establishing and learning the 6 times table facts

Practising the words *multiples* and *multiply*

Materials

Calculator

Scissors and glue (glue stick)

Envelope (to keep tables cards in)

Number line to 60 (optional: for supporting activity)

Supporting activities

▶ Count forwards and backwards on the number line in sixes out loud.

▶ Use the cards made from Copymaster Y46 to practise the 6 times table.

Using the textbook pages

These pages follow a similar pattern to those on the 2 times table (Blue Textbook 2 pages 10 and 11), the 5 times table (Blue Textbook 2 pages 24 and 25), the 3 times table (Blue Textbook 3 pages 18 and 19), the 10 times table (Green Textbook 1 pages 12 and 13) and the 4 times table (Green Textbook 3 pages 8 and 9).

Questions 1 to 17 emphasise each tables fact through a picture, and by adding six repeatedly, and lastly by multiplying on a calculator. Children can see that, whichever way you work it out, the answer is the same. Question 18 asks the reverse question (leading to division), 'How many beetles?'.

Answers **1** 6 **2** 6 **3** 18 **4** 18 **5** 18 **6** 24 **7** 24 **8** 24 **9** 36 **10** 36 **11** 36 **12** 42 **13** 42 **14** 42 **15** 48 **16** 48 **17** 48 **18** 9 **19** 54 **20** 54 **21** Child's copy of the 6 times table

Using the copymasters

Copymaster Y46 This sheet makes 11 small cards, with a tables question on one side and the answer on the other. Provide each child with an envelope to keep them in. Show children how to practise: shuffle the cards and put them in a pile, questions up. Answer the top question, then turn over to see if you got it right. If you did, put it to one side; if not, put it at the bottom of the pile to try again. Then use the cards the other way up – look at the answer, and say what the question is. Use the cards as frequently as you wish. Children can work on them individually, or with a partner, or take them home to practise.

Copymaster Y47 Children who feel confident can use this sheet as a test. Those who still need support should use a calculator to check as they go along.

Multiplying

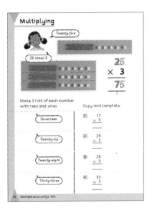 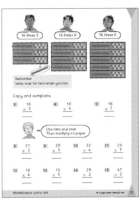  

Textbook pages 22 and 23   Copymasters Y48 and Y49

Purpose

Using tens and ones equipment, to multiply 2-digit numbers by 2, 3, 4 or 5

Practising one method of pencil and paper multiplication, showing how it links with using equipment

Materials

Tens and ones (such as Multibase or Dienes')

Calculator

Supporting activity

▶ Make up 5 more sums like the ones on textbook page 23 for a friend to do. Check them with a calculator.

Using the textbook pages

The pencil and paper method of multiplying used here, was introduced in Yellow Textbook 1, in 'More multiplying' on pages 24 and 25. Tens and ones equipment is used to remind children of the link between multiplication and repeated addition. Using the equipment alongside pencil and paper multiplication helps children understand the method, especially in examples where they need to exchange single ones for tens, and 'carry'.

Questions 1 to 15 do not all require 'carrying'. Questions 1 to 4 use just the 3 times table; questions 5 to 15 use a mixture of 2s, 3s, 4s and 5s. Some children may need to use a tables square to help them, if their mental recall of tables facts is not yet secure. The most important focus here should be on understanding and using the pencil and paper method.

Answers **1** 51 **2** 78 **3** 84 **4** 99 **5** 48 **6** 64 **7** 80 **8** 42 **9** 87 **10** 88 **11** 100 **12** 72 **13** 65 **14** 58 **15** 94

Using the copymasters

Copymasters Y48 and Y49 Further practice using tens and ones, pencil and paper, and a calculator.

What's missing?

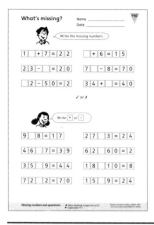
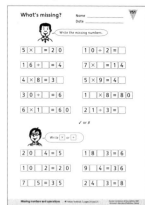

Textbook pages 24 and 25   Copymasters Y50, Y51, Y60, Y61 and Y62

Purpose

Finding ways of solving 'missing number' problems

Finding missing operations (+, –, × or ÷)

Developing understanding of place value

Materials

Tens and ones (such as Multibase or Dienes')

Calculator

Supporting activity

▶ Play the 'What's missing?' game. See Copymasters Y60, Y61 and Y62 below.

Using the textbook pages

Many children find missing number problems, even those which seem very obvious to an adult, quite baffling. These pages use two methods to develop children's skills at solving them: using tens and ones equipment to help visualise the original sum, and making up problems of their own using cards, in the 'What's missing?' game. In addition, children should be strongly encouraged to use 'trial and improvement' – in other words, to try a number or operation, to see if it works, and to keep experimenting until they find the solution.

For each question, encourage children to use tens and ones to experiment, if they cannot see straight away what the missing number should be. They should use a calculator to check each sum as they go along. Many children find the questions where the missing number is first, more difficult than those where it comes after the operation.

Questions 9 to 15 are more difficult than questions 1 to 8. Some children will find it helpful to play the 'What's missing?' game *before* doing questions 9 to 15.

Questions like numbers 12, 13 and 14, where attention is focussed on the tens or units place in the sum, help develop children's understanding of place value.

Answers **1** 6 **2** 4 **3** 9 **4** 8 **5** + **6** – **7** – **8** + **9** 38 – 8 = 30 **10** 34 + 6 = 40 **11** 15 + 5 = 20 **12** 32 – 30 = 2 **13** 48 – 8 = 40 **14** 25 – 20 = 5 **15** It could be + or ×

Using the copymasters

Copymasters Y50 and Y51 Further practice.

Copymasters Y60, Y61 and Y62 The 'What's missing?' game can be played as a game for two, or the equipment can be used by a child working on their own. The game can be played as many times as you wish, from these pages onwards.

Dividing marbles

Textbook pages 26 and 27

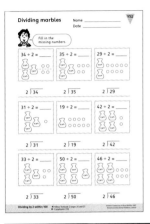 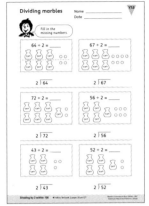

Copymasters Y52 and Y53

Purpose

Practising dividing by 2, using a practical context, and writing the divisions in this format: $2\overline{)24}$

Materials

Marbles (about 50) and 4 small bags (optional: for supporting activity)

Supporting activity

▶ Put ten marbles in each of four small paper or plastic bags. Use the bags of marbles and some single ones to do questions 1 to 16 on textbook pages 26 and 27.

Using the textbook pages

Division using this layout: $2\overline{)14}$ was introduced in 'More tables stars' on textbook pages 14 and 15, using examples which were all within the range of tables facts practised so far. These pages extend the work to division of numbers up to 100, but keeping to division by 2, until the method is well established. Initially, the examples used are all related to the bags of marbles and single marbles shown. The pictures are provided to help children see that when we divide, we do not always have to split everything into single items; we can often share things whilst they are still grouped in tens. The context of marbles (which cannot be cut in half) means that there will be a remainder of 1 in some questions.

Many children will be able to answer each question using a combination of the pictures provided and their own mental skill at halving. Encourage children who need more support to draw bags of ten marbles and single marbles, and then put in a dotted line to split them into two shares. Children should do the questions in numerical order, especially for questions 1 to 6 and 11 to 16, so they are alternately looking at a picture then at the division written more formally.

The example on textbook page 27, after question 16, shows what happens when there is an odd number of tens – we have to split a ten into ones.

'More dividing', on textbook pages 28 and 29, moves on to the next step – using tens and ones equipment to explain a pencil and paper method.

Answers **1** 12 **2** 12 **3** 13 **4** 13 **5** 14 **6** 14 **7** 10 **8** 10 r.1 **9** 11 **10** 11 r.1 **11** 22 **12** 22 **13** 22 r.1 **14** 22 r.1 **15** 24 **16** 24 **17** 27 **18** 27 **19** 27 r.1

Using the copymasters

Copymasters Y52 and Y53 Further practice, showing two ways of writing each division and matching pictorial representations.

Dividing by 2 within 100

More dividing

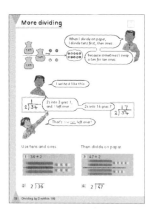
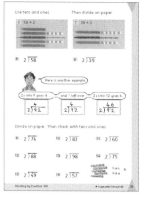

Textbook pages 28 and 29

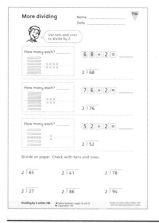
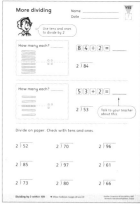

Copymasters Y54 and Y55

Purpose

Using tens and ones equipment, to divide 2-digit numbers by 2
Introducing a pencil and paper method of dividing 2-digit numbers by 2, showing how it links with using equipment

Materials

Tens and ones (such as Multibase or Dienes')
Calculator

Supporting activity

► Make up 5 more questions like those on textbook page 29 for a friend to do. Check them using tens and ones equipment.

Using the textbook pages

On the previous two pages in this book, in 'Dividing marbles', children practised dividing by 2 with pictures to represent the divisions, and using this layout: $2\overline{)24}$, to write down their questions and answers. These pages move on to the next step, providing the teacher with an opportunity to explain a standard pencil and paper method of dividing, including 'carrying'. It is important, though, that children know there are several effective ways of finding the answer to any sum; the method explained on page 28 is very useful, but it is not the only way of doing these.

Make sure that children do use equipment for questions 1, 3, 5 and 7, even though there are illustrations of tens and ones, as it helps to make sure they understand what they are doing.

Some children may need the word 'example' explaining to them: that it is another question all worked out, to show them how these can be done. Use nine tens and two ones to demonstrate what is happening in the pencil and paper method, including swapping a ten for ten ones when you 'carry'.

Answers **1** 18 **2** 18 **3** 23 r.1 **4** 23 r.1 **5** 29 **6** 29 **7** 19 r.1 **8** 19 r.1 **9** 37 **10** 41 r.1 **11** 30 **12** 44 **13** 49 **14** 37 r.1 **15** 24 r.1 **16** 28 r.1

Using the copymasters

Copymaster Y54 Further examples using equipment, pencil and paper, and a calculator (even number examples only).

Copymaster Y55 As above, but including an odd number example when dividing with a calculator. Children may need reminding that the calculator writes ' .5' instead of one half.

Nines and tens

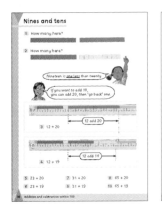

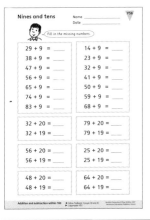

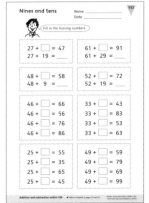

Textbook pages 30 and 31   Copymasters Y56 and Y57

Purpose

Practising addition and subtraction within 100 using a variety of methods
Establishing and practising a mental method of adding 19

Materials

Tens and ones (such as Multibase or Dienes')
Number line marked 0 to 100 (optional: for supporting activity)
Calculator (optional: for supporting activity)

Supporting activity

▶ Work with a friend. Put tens and ones on a number line to make any number up to one hundred. Ask your friend to take away 19. Check with a calculator.

Using the textbook pages

'Adding nine', on pages 22 and 23 of Yellow Textbook 1, looked at a mental method of adding nine, by adding ten and taking one away. These pages show how a similar method can be used to add nineteen, or twenty-nine.

It is helpful to use a number line to work through the example on page 30.

Check that children notice that questions 11 to 19, where they are adding 30, are very similar to questions 20 to 28, where they are adding 29!

As illustrated, some children may wish to write questions 29 to 40 in a vertical format to add them.

Answers **1** 20 **2** 19 **3** 32 **4** 31 **5** 43 **6** 42 **7** 51 **8** 50 **9** 85 **10** 84 **11** 51 **12** 65 **13** 73 **14** 76 **15** 88 **16** 49 **17** 54 **18** 92 **19** 100 **20** 50 **21** 64 **22** 72 **23** 75 **24** 87 **25** 48 **26** 53 **27** 91 **28** 99 **29** 96 **30** 95 **31** 57 **32** 56 **33** 88 **34** 87 **35** 71 **36** 70 **37** 86 **38** 85 **39** 59 **40** 58

Using the copymasters

Copymaster Y56 Adding nines, nineteens and twenties.

Copymaster Y57 Missing number problems which particularly emphasise adding multiples of ten.

Textbook 2 page 32

Make one hundred

Textbook page 32

Purpose

Practising finding numbers which add to one hundred

Materials

Tens and ones (such as Multibase or Dienes')
Cards numbered 1 to 100
Calculator

Using the textbook page

This page provides a game which encourages children to think about pairs of numbers which make one hundred. It is unlikely that any child will use subtraction as their preferred method of finding the number they need to add to another number to make one hundred; it is usually more efficient to 'count on'.

The most common mistake with these problems when done mentally is to give an answer which is ten too big; using the tens and ones equipment to make the number on the card, helps children get the right answer, and can improve their ability to visualise problems like this when they do not have equipment available.

The game can be played as many times as you wish.

Yellow Textbook 3 / Copymasters Y63–Y92

Contents

◻ Counting and place value

◼ Addition and subtraction

● Multiplication and division

◕ Mixed operations

Textbook 3 pages 4 and 5

Two hundred

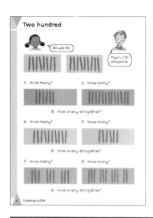

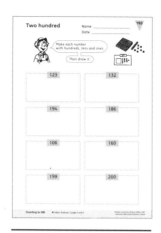

Textbook pages 4 and 5   Copymaster Y63

Purpose

Practising counting numbers of objects, up to 200

Practising counting in tens

Checking confidence in using hundreds, tens and ones equipment

Developing understanding of place value

Materials

Hundreds, tens and ones (such as Multibase or Dienes')

Multilink, centicubes or other similar cubes (optional: for supporting activity)

Supporting activities

▶ Work with a friend. Each make a square using one hundred cubes. Put one square on top of the other, so that you have 200 cubes stacked together neatly. Now each make a pile of another 100 cubes, and put your two piles together. Which looks most – 200 stacked cubes, or 200 cubes in a pile?

▶ Play the 'Make 200' game on textbook page 5.

Using the textbook pages

Introduce these pages by looking at the ones, tens and hundreds from structured counting equipment, to make sure children know that one hundred single ones, or ten tens, make one hundred. Most children find counting in tens up to one hundred very straightforward, but are less confident after that. A few very confident children may add their answers, for example, to questions 1 and 2 to get the answer for question 3; most children will count all the tens again.

The 'Make 200' game on page 5 helps develop children's understanding of place value, as they have to think about which number card should be the tens or ones figure in the 2-digit number they are making. The game practises counting, including exchanging ten ones for a ten, and ten tens for a hundred. The game can be played as many times as you wish from this page onwards.

(NB Any child who has difficulty counting the amounts in questions 1 to 9 should be given further practical work, *before* continuing with work in this book. Yellow Textbook 2 includes activities to practise counting up to 180.)

Answers **1** 60 **2** 130 **3** 190 **4** 100 **5** 60 **6** 160 **7** 90 **8** 110 **9** 200

Using the copymaster

Copymaster Y63 Making numbers with equipment, then drawing them. Drawing not only provides a record of the child's practical activity, but also gives many children a mental picture of each number, which can help with developing their ability at mental arithmetic.

Saving

Textbook pages 6 and 7   Copymasters Y64 and Y65

Purpose

Revising writing amounts of money using £ and a decimal point, or p

Finding the difference between two amounts of money, using coins

Multiplying amounts of money, using own preferred method

Materials

Coins (about £5 in mixed denominations under £1, and £20 in '£1 coins' – which could be represented by counters, if necessary)

Supporting activity

▶ Make up 5 more questions like the ones on textbook page 6 for a friend to do.

Using the textbook pages

'Half price sale', on pages 8 and 9 in Yellow Textbook 2, practised using coins and notes for amounts of money in pounds and pence. These pages also practise handling coins, but concentrate on 'adding on' to find the difference between two amounts of money. This method is the most common one used by adults and children (instead of subtraction) when calculating change or, as in this context, finding out how much more is needed to reach a total.

Questions 1 to 8 can be done mentally; many people develop different mental methods for money problems than those for more abstract number work. Encourage children to explain how they found the answer to each question, and to demonstrate what they did with coins, if possible.

Questions 9 to 11 are multiplication problems, which children may use a variety of methods to answer, including repeated addition on paper, or making piles of coins for each week or month and then counting the total.

Answers **1** 40p **2** £1.49 **3** £2.60 **4** £2.30 **5** £8.50 **6** £20.70 **7** £18.00 **8** £9.75 **9** £6.00 **10** £18.00 **11** £16.00

Using the copymasters

Copymaster Y64 Further practice at multiplying amounts of money.

Copymaster Y65 Questions to make up for a friend to do, like the ones on Copymaster Y64. This sheet can be repeated as many times as wished from these pages onwards.

Textbook 3 pages 8 and 9

Teen sums

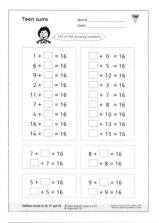
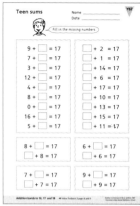

| Textbook pages 8 and 9 | Copymasters Y66, Y67, Y88 and Y89 |

Purpose

Establishing and practising addition bonds to 16, 17 and 18, and improving immediate mental recall of those number facts

Materials

Cubes (about 20 each of 2 different colours)

Supporting activity

▶ Play the 'Eighteens' game. See Copymasters Y88 and Y89 below.

Using the textbook pages

Addition bonds to 15 were practised in 'Games', on pages 10 and 11 of Green Textbook 3. These pages look at three sets of addition bonds at once, since many people find it easier to work out the bonds for 16, 17 and 18 by using a selection of very speedy mental methods, rather than learning them off by heart in the same way as they have done for smaller numbers.

Questions 1 to 20 concentrate on using doubling to help find the answer when adding a pair of consecutive numbers. Questions 21 to 34 focus upon a different mental method – of making ten, then adding the remainder of the second number. Encourage children to use cubes if they want to, to do at least some of these sums, as the practical activity can help improve their ability to do these sums mentally.

If any child needs further practice with addition and subtraction bonds to 15, use the 'Speedy sums' tests from Green Textbook 3, made from Copymaster G71, for revision.

Answers **1** 14 **2** 15 **3** 12 **4** 13 **5** 16 **6** 17 **7** 18 **8** 19 **9** 12 **10** 14 **11** 16 **12** 18 **13** 17 **14** 13 **15** 19 **16** 15 **17** 13 **18** 19 **19** 15 **20** 17 **21** 15 **22** 13 **23** 13 **24** 17 **25** 14 **26** 15 **27** 13 **28** 13 **29** 17 **30** 14 **31** No **32** Yes **33** Yes **34** Yes

Using the copymasters

Copymaster Y66 Children who feel confident with number bonds to 16 can use this sheet as a test. Those who still need help can use cubes or fingers.

Copymaster Y67 This sheet is like Copymaster Y66, but for number bonds to 17.

Copymasters Y88 and Y89 The 'Eighteens' game. This is similar to the game called 'Fifteens' in Green Textbook 3. It can be played as many times as you wish from these pages onwards.

Textbook 3 pages 10 and 11

Halves

Textbook pages 10 and 11   Copymasters Y68 and Y69

Purpose
Practising halving numbers within 120
Revising general knowledge number facts
Comparing practical, mental and calculator methods for halving

Materials
Counters
Calculator

Supporting activity
▶ Make up some 'half my age' questions like the ones on textbook page 11, for a friend to do.

Using the textbook pages
Halving was last practised when dividing by 2 within 100 in 'Dividing marbles', on pages 26 and 27 of Yellow Textbook 2.

These pages start by halving even numbers, then revising *dozen*, the number of minutes in an hour, months in a year, and pence in a pound.

Question 15 gives children the opportunity to think of any other special number words they know (for example, *century*) or number facts, or to make up practical halving problems.

Questions 16 to 20 are about comparative ages. Question 20 may usefully lead to a discussion about the fact that each person gets one year older each year; that people's ages may seem to get closer together or further apart at different times of the year because their birthdays are in different months, but the actual difference in two ages (especially if you count it to the nearest month) stays the same. In any person's life, though, there can only be one year at the most, where they are half the age of another particular person.

Answers **1** 9 **2** 23 **3** 45 **4** 47 **5** 55 **6** 41 **7** 33 **8** 60 **9** 6 **10** 30 **11** 6 **12** 50p **13** 4 **14** 29 **15** Child's own questions **16** 17 **17** 14 **18** 38 **19** Child's age and information about child half their age **20** No (see notes above)

Using the copymasters
Copymaster Y68 Further questions on halving, and some 'working backwards' – i.e. doubling to find the number which was halved.

Copymaster Y69 Halving using pictorial representation, practical equipment and a calculator alongside each other. The context of sharing biscuits should encourage children to see that there does not have to be a remainder for any of these questions. They are also reminded that one half can be written as $\frac{1}{2}$ or as .5.

Speedy tables

Textbook pages 12 and 13

Copymaster Y70

Purpose

Establishing or revising multiplication and division bonds for the 0, 1, 2, 3, 4, 5 and 10 times tables, and 6s within 36

Materials

Stopwatch or 3, 2 and 1 minute sand timers (some children may have digital watches with timers on them)

Calculator

Two 1 to 6 dice (optional: for supporting activity)

Supporting activity

▶ Practise your tables from 1 x 1 to 6 x 6 with two dice. Throw the dice; multiply the two numbers, and check your answer on a calculator to see if you were right.

Using the textbook pages

These pages continue a series of timed tests used in Yellow Textbooks 1 and 2, to improve mental recall of tables facts. Questions 1 to 20 should be read to the child who is answering them, to help them improve their ability to take in and remember questions without seeing them in print. Some children find it very difficult to listen and concentrate; it can help them if their partner stops after questions 7 and 14, to mark them before going on. Marking sums with a calculator helps children remember any they got wrong; it also reminds them that it is quicker to do these smaller sums in your head than on a calculator.

Answers **1** 30 **2** 35 **3** 8 **4** 18 **5** 18 **6** 0 **7** 40 **8** 7 **9** 4 **10** 3 **11** 6 **12** 5 **13** 9 **14** 9 **15** 36 **16** 1 **17** 45 **18** 4 **19** 80 **20** 5 **21** 4 **22** 9 **23** 2 **24** 5 **25** 6 **26** 7 **27** 5 **28** 2 **29** 6 **30** 1 **31** 10 **32** 7 **33** 4 **34** 3 **35** 8

Using the copymaster

Copymaster Y70 This provides two parallel tests covering all the significant tables facts as listed. Children should fill in their name and the date first, and then time the test. The timing can be done by the teacher; alternatively, two children can take it in turns to time each other.

At first, allow children 3 minutes to do as much as they can (and ring the 3 in the top left-hand corner of the test sheet). Repeating the tests, a few days apart, is a very effective way of helping children learn these off by heart, and their scores usually improve quite quickly. When a child has scored 20 on a test, reduce the time when they next try it to 2 minutes, then finally, if wished, to 1 minute. Children should always be trying to beat *their own* previous score or time, not to beat another child. The latter can encourage cheating, and so is not as effective.

Printing

  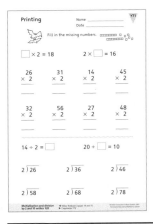 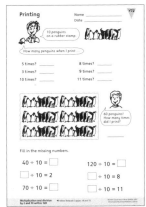

Textbook pages 14 and 15 *Copymasters Y71 and Y72*

Purpose

Practising multiplying by 2 within 120, including using a vertical layout

Practising dividing by 2 within 120, using both this: $2\overline{)34}$

and this: $34 \div 2 =$ layout (multiples of 2 only)

Practising multiplying and dividing by 10 within 120 (multiples of 10 only)

Materials

Calculator

Tens and ones (such as Multibase or Dienes')

Printing stamps and ink pad (optional: for supporting activity)

Supporting activity

▶ Use a printing stamp with two (or ten) animals or shapes on it to do some printing of your own, and count how many you have printed.

Using the textbook pages

If possible, introduce these pages by doing some printing in twos or tens. The context of printing is used to think about multiplication and division, and to practise several ways of writing these questions, and of answering them. Because of the context, none of the questions require children to think about 'remainders' or fractions. Here, children concentrate on the 2 and 10 times tables; later on, in 'More printing' on pages 20 and 21 in this textbook, they will use the 3 times table.

Some children may find it helpful to use tens and ones equipment to support their pencil and paper arithmetic, especially for divisions involving 'carrying'. This was introduced in Yellow Textbook 2, 'More dividing', on pages 28 and 29.

Answers **1** 14 **2** 18 **3** 26 **4** 52 **5** 44 **6** 70 **7** 82 **8** 76 **9** 108 **10** 120 **11** 19 **12** 27 **13** 34 **14** 55

Using the copymasters

Copymaster Y71 Further practice with the 2 times table.

Copymaster Y72 Further practice with the 10 times table.

Textbook 3 pages 16 and 17

Sums to twenty

 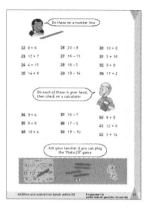 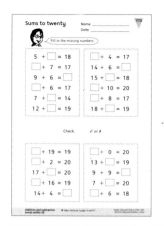

Textbook pages 16 and 17   Copymasters Y73, Y90, Y91 and Y92

Purpose

Establishing and practising addition and subtraction bonds within 20
Improving immediate mental recall of those number facts

Materials

Tens and ones (such as Multibase or Dienes')
Calculator
Number line (numbered to 20 or more)

Supporting activity

▶ Play the 'Make 20' game. See Copymasters Y90, Y91 and Y92 below.

Using the textbook pages

Addition bonds to 18 were practised in 'Teen sums', on pages 8 and 9 of this textbook. Those pages commented on the fact that many people find it easier to work out the bonds for 16, 17, 18 (and 19 and 20) by using a selection of very speedy mental methods, rather than learning them off by heart in the same way as they have done for numbers up to 15.

Questions 1 to 9 are all sums within 15, so children should be confident with doing these in their heads. If they have difficulty, use the 'Speedy sums' tests from Green Textbook 3, made from Copymaster G71, for revision.

Questions 10 to 21 revise using tens and ones, and questions 22 to 33 revise the use of a number line. Both these types of equipment can provide useful mental images when a child is doing arithmetic in their head. If possible, talk to children about the methods they have used for questions 34 to 42.

Answers **1** 7 **2** 15 **3** 10 **4** 12 **5** 14 **6** 9 **7** 7 **8** 7 **9** 14 **10** 19 **11** 7 **12** 18 **13** 8 **14** 20 **15** 18 **16** 9 **17** 15 **18** 19 **19** 6 **20** 12 **21** 17 **22** 14 **23** 19 **24** 19 **25** 20 **26** 11 **27** 3 **28** 13 **29** 5 **30** 18 **31** 19 **32** 18 **33** 19 **34** 13 **35** 16 **36** 20 **37** 9 **38** 14 **39** 9 **40** 17 **41** 18 **42** 17

Using the copymasters

Copymaster Y73 Children who feel confident with number bonds within 20 can use this sheet as a test. Those who still need help can use tens and ones, or fingers.

Copymasters Y90, Y91 and Y92 The 'Make 20' game. Each time they have a turn, children practise adding two numbers within 20 in their head, then find the difference between that total and 20, using equipment. The game can be played as many times as you wish from these pages onwards.

Cheesecakes

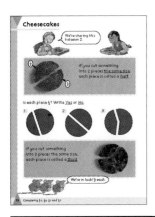 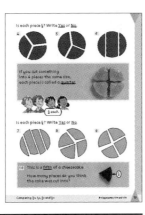  

Textbook pages 18 and 19   Copymasters Y74 and Y75

Purpose

Revising halves and quarters
Introducing or revising thirds and fifths
Comparing the sizes of different fractions

Materials

Ruler and rubber
Circle stencil or compasses, and scissors (optional: for supporting activity)

Supporting activity

▶ Draw four circles the same size, using a stencil or compasses. Cut them out. Cut one circle into halves (you could fold or draw on lines, if you want to). Put the pieces on top of each other: did you manage to make them *exactly* the same size, so they really are halves? Repeat this with the other circles, to make thirds, quarters and fifths. Which ones were easy, and which were difficult?

Using the textbook pages

Quarters were last tackled in Yellow Textbook 1, in 'Quarter each' on pages 30 and 31; halving numbers has been practised regularly, including in 'Halves' earlier in this textbook, on pages 10 and 11.

Food is one of the most natural contexts for work on fractions of a 'whole one' with children. These pages revise halves and quarters, particularly emphasising that fractions are named according to how many pieces the 'whole one' is divided into, *and* that those pieces must be exactly the same size as each other. Thirds and fifths are introduced following the same pattern. Point out that the more pieces a cake is divided into, the smaller each piece will be. The supporting activity described above may be essential with some children, so that they can check that pieces are the same size by putting them on top of each other.

Answers **1** No **2** Yes **3** No **4** Yes **5** No **6** No **7** No **8** No **9** Yes **10** Five

Using the copymasters

Copymaster Y74 Children may need to draw their lines several times (hence the suggestion that they use pencil!) before they feel confident that they have got the circles divided equally, especially for thirds and fifths.

Copymaster Y75 Marks are placed on these circles to enable children to draw accurate diagrams, as these are essential in order to compare fractions. Make sure they realise that the 'whole ones' here are exactly the same size; otherwise, it might not be true that one half is bigger than one quarter (for example, a quarter of a big cheesecake could be bigger than half a little one).

Comparing $\frac{1}{2}$s, $\frac{1}{3}$s, $\frac{1}{4}$s and $\frac{1}{5}$s

Textbook 3 pages 20 and 21

More printing

  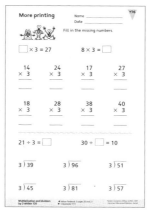 

Textbook pages 20 and 21   Copymasters Y76 and Y77

Purpose

Practising multiplying by 3 within 120, including using a vertical layout
Practising dividing by 3 within 120, using both this: $3 \overline{)42}$
and this: $42 \div 3 =$ layout (multiples of 3 only)

Materials

Calculator
Tens and ones (such as Multibase or Dienes')
Printing stamps and ink pad (optional: for supporting activity)

Supporting activity

▶ Use a printing stamp with three animals or shapes on it to do some printing of your own, and count how many you have printed.

Using the textbook pages

These pages follow on from 'Printing', on pages 14 and 15 of this textbook, which concentrated on multiples of 2 and 10. The context of printing is used to think about multiplication and division, and to practise several ways of writing and answering these questions. Because of the context, none of the questions require children to think about 'remainders' or fractions.

Some children may find it helpful to use tens and ones equipment to support their pencil and paper arithmetic, especially for divisions involving 'carrying'.

Answers **1** 18 **2** 21 **3** 24 **4** 30 **5** 33 **6** 39 **7** 45 **8** 48 **9** 57 **10** 72 **11** 12 **12** 16 **13** 30 **14** 25

Using the copymasters

Copymasters Y76 and Y77 Further practice with the 3 times table.

Number cards

  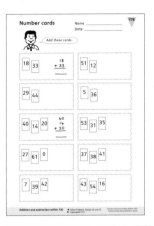 

Textbook pages 22 and 23   *Copymasters Y78 and Y79*

Purpose

Practising addition and subtraction within 120, including using a pencil and paper method

Materials

Cards numbered 0 to 40

Hundreds, tens and ones (such as Multibase or Dienes')

Calculator

Supporting activities

▶ Play the 'Choose 2 numbers' game on textbook page 23.

▶ Use cards numbered 0 to 40 to make up more addition and subtraction sums like the ones on textbook page 22.

Using the textbook pages

Ordinary playing cards have been used in earlier textbooks to practise adding (for example, in 'Four cards', pages 18 and 19 of Green Textbook 3). Cards numbered 0 to 40 enable children to do additions within 80, using two cards, or addition within 120, using three cards. Many children will find it helpful to write the sums on page 22 using a vertical layout, so that they can use pencil and paper methods to add if they wish. Some children will also want to use tens and ones equipment.

The 'Choose 2 numbers' game on page 23 provides children with the opportunity to practise adding using mental or pencil and paper methods. Encourage children to talk about how they have done their sums, and to discuss which sums they are able to do easily in their heads, and which ones need pencil and paper or equipment. The game can be played as many times as you wish from these pages onwards.

Answers 1 34 **2** 35 **3** 33 **4** 31 **5** 70 **6** 18 **7** 54 **8** 51 **9** 26 **10** 22 **11** 14 **12** 16 **13** 19 **14** 23

Using the copymasters

Copymaster Y78 Further practice at adding two or three numbers.

Copymaster Y79 Practising taking away, including writing the question in a vertical layout.

Textbook 3 pages 24 and 25

Guinea pig sums

Textbook pages 24 and 25   Copymasters Y80 and Y81

Purpose
Revising repeated addition with 3s and 4s (the 3 and 4 times tables)

Practising addition with combinations of 3s and 4s

Practising multiplication by 3 and by 4, including in a vertical layout

Materials
Book about small pets (optional: for supporting activity)

Supporting activity
▶ Can you find out how many toes other pets have? You could look in a book, or ask a pet owner. Make up some sums using those numbers.

Using the textbook pages
Many children who have pet guinea pigs are surprised to find that these animals do not have five toes, and even more surprised that they have different numbers on their front and back feet. If possible, it is interesting to introduce these pages by looking at a real guinea pig.

Questions 1 to 15 provide a mixture of addition and multiplication practice using threes and fours. Most children answer question 4 by 'trial and improvement': they guess how many guinea pigs it might be, then add or multiply to see if they are right, and if not, they make their guess larger or smaller.

Questions 16 to 18 are small investigations; although each question only asks for *one* sum which makes each of those numbers, there are several possible answers for each one, and some children may want to find more possibilities.

Answers **1** 14 **2** 28 **3** 42 **4** 5 **5** 56 **6** 10 **7** 11 **8** 12 **9** 12 **10** 15 **11** 18 **12** 21 **13** 16 **14** 19 **15** 19 **16** to **18** Child's own sums to make 14, 22 and 25

Using the copymasters
Copymaster Y80 Further practice at addition.

Copymaster Y81 Further practice at multiplication by 3 or 4.

Textbook 3 pages 26 and 27

Inches and halves

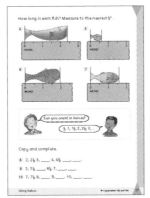

Textbook pages 26 and 27

Copymasters Y82 and Y83

Purpose

Using halves on a 'number line' (a ruler)

Counting in halves within 20

Measuring in inches to the nearest half inch

Materials

Scissors and glue (glue stick)

Ruler marked in inches (optional: for supporting activity)

Supporting activity

▶ Find a ruler marked in inches. Does it have half-inches marked on it, like the tape measure made from Copymaster Y82? Use it to measure some things in your classroom.

Using the textbook pages

Even though we predominantly use the metric system for measurement in school, many children have experience of using inches elsewhere, particularly as some toy catalogues give sizes of toys in inches, and some children's clothing is marked in inches. Make sure that children realise that inches are part of an old system of measuring length, which has been replaced by the metric system in many situations.

The inch ruler acts as a number line in just the same way as the centimetre ruler in 'Rulers', on pages 28 and 29 of Red Textbook 3. Inches are a more useful context for halves than centimetres, though. This is because it is more natural to use $\frac{1}{2}$ with inches, and because there is enough space on an inch tape for children to write in every number themselves.

Check that children know that the abbreviation for inch/es is ". For questions 4, 5 and 7, discuss what we mean by 'to the nearest half inch'.

Answers **1** $3\frac{1}{2}$" **2** $1\frac{1}{2}$" **3** $2\frac{1}{2}$" **4** $2\frac{1}{2}$" **5** $\frac{1}{2}$" **6** 2" **7** $1\frac{1}{2}$" **8** 2, $2\frac{1}{2}$, 3, $3\frac{1}{2}$, 4, $4\frac{1}{2}$, 5, $5\frac{1}{2}$ **9** 5, $5\frac{1}{2}$, 6, $6\frac{1}{2}$, 7, $7\frac{1}{2}$, 8 **10** 7, $7\frac{1}{2}$, 8, $8\frac{1}{2}$, 9, $9\frac{1}{2}$, 10, $10\frac{1}{2}$, 11

Using the copymasters

Copymaster Y82 Use this sheet to make an 18 inch tape measure, which can then be used to measure various objects in the classroom. Check that children measure from the zero mark on the tape, *not* from the end of the tape.

Copymaster Y83 Further measuring practice; counting in halves in order, to do a dot-to-dot.

Using halves

Textbook 3 pages 28 and 29

Café

Textbook pages 28 and 29   Copymasters Y84 and Y85

Purpose

Using a table (in the form of a menu) to collect and use information about choices and prices

Using role play to develop understanding of real-life experience, and to give practice in using money and bills

Materials

Token notes and coins (for example, five £5 notes, ten £1 coins, and other mixed coins totalling about £5)

Supporting activity

▶ Talk about any times you have been to a café to eat. What choices of food were there? What did you have? How much did it cost?

Using the textbook pages

'Day trip' on pages 28 and 29 of Green Textbook 3, used role play to learn about buying and selling tickets for excursions. Pages 28 and 29 here should be used to make sure children understand the information given on the menu, and how a bill is drawn up. They can then use Copymasters Y84 and Y85 to run their own café.

For questions 8 to 12, using a calculator could be confusing for some children since these examples include prices in both pounds and pence; instead, encourage children to use notes to help them.

Answers **1** Child's choice of flavour **2** 70p **3** 80p **4** 60p **5** £1.40 **6** 30p **7** 60p **8** £1.40 **9** 90p **10** £1.20 **11** £2.40 **12** Child's choice for up to £2

Using the copymasters

Copymaster Y84 This sheet provides an outline for children to make up their own prices for a menu, using the one on textbook page 28 as a model. It can be completed by two children working together.

Copymaster Y85 Cut out these bills; you may need several sets. The 'café owners' will need some token notes and coins, the menu, bills, and perhaps a pencil and notebook. Work in a group of 2, 3 or 4. If 2 people are 'café owners', 2 can be customers. The customers say what they want to eat and drink; the owners write out the bills, take money and give change. Change roles after each transaction.

Textbook 3 pages 30 and 31

Halves and quarters

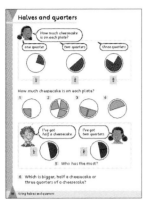 

Textbook pages 30 and 31

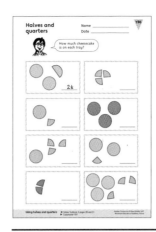 

Copymasters Y86 and Y87

Purpose

Revising quarters, and using $\frac{1}{4}$, $\frac{2}{4}$, and $\frac{3}{4}$

Seeing that $\frac{2}{4}$ is equivalent to $\frac{1}{2}$

Using quarters on a number line (a ruler)

Measuring in inches to the nearest quarter inch

Counting in quarters within 6

Materials

Ruler marked in inches (optional: for supporting activity)

Supporting activities

▶ Look at a ruler marked in inches. Has it got marks every quarter of an inch?

▶ Finish the textbook pages first. Then find the tape measure you made from Copymaster Y82 for textbook page 27, and mark the quarter inches on your tape, up to 6", like the ruler at the top of textbook page 31.

Using the textbook pages

These pages bring together the work earlier in this textbook on halves and quarters, from 'Cheesecakes' on pages 18 and 19, and 'Inches and halves' on pages 26 and 27, and extend the work on quarters in the context of inches.

Questions 1 to 4 revise writing $\frac{1}{4}$, $\frac{2}{4}$, $\frac{3}{4}$ and $\frac{1}{2}$. Some children may already be confident that one half is equivalent to two quarters, and may answer $\frac{1}{2}$ to question 3. When children do questions 5 and 6, make sure they realise that all the 'whole ones' here are exactly the same size; otherwise, it might not be true that three quarters is bigger than one half (for example, one half of a big cheesecake could be bigger than three quarters of a little one).

Questions 7 to 10 require children to write mixed numbers (for example, $1\frac{1}{4}$), as they did for the questions on textbook pages 26 and 27. Check their handwriting, to make sure they realise that the numbers in the fraction should be written quite small, so that the fraction is the same height as the whole number.

Answers **1** $\frac{1}{4}$ **2** $\frac{3}{4}$ **3** $\frac{2}{4}$ or $\frac{1}{2}$ **4** $\frac{1}{2}$ **5** They have the same amount **6** $\frac{3}{4}$
7 4" **8** $1\frac{1}{4}$" **9** $2\frac{3}{4}$" **10** $3\frac{3}{4}$"

Using the copymasters

Copymaster Y86 Using mixed numbers to count cheesecakes.

Copymaster Y87 Measuring to the nearest quarter inch, and counting in halves and quarters within 6.

Cubes in groups

Textbook page 32

Purpose

Revising times tables facts within 20, through grouping

Investigating divisibility by 2, 3, 4, 5 and 6, within 20

Materials

Cubes

Using the textbook page

This page provides an activity which encourages children to think about grouping within various numbers, so that they realise that some numbers can be divided into exact groups in several ways, whilst others cannot.

Children may work best in pairs, so that they can decide together, for example, whether they think 14 cubes *will* divide exactly into groups of 4, and then try it.

Check that children organise their drawings so that it is clear which number of cubes they were using altogether, and how many they were putting in each group, and whether it worked or not.

Ask children whether they found any numbers which they could not put in 2s, 3s, 4s, 5s, *or* 6s. If wished, ask them to try all the numbers up to 20, and to make a list of the numbers which cannot be grouped in this way. (They should find it is 7, 11, 13, 17 and 19.)

Progress tests

The copiable Progress tests on the next six pages can be used in a variety of ways. There are two parallel tests for each textbook, using similar questions but with different numbers. This enables you to give alternative versions to children who are sitting next to each other, when more than one child is ready to try the test at the same time. It also means that you can use one version as a practice or revision exercise, if you wish.

The tests are intended to be used primarily as one way of showing children that they are making progress, and should be given after a child has completed all the work in each textbook. Where a context for a problem is used in a test, it is always one which the child has previously met in the textbook or associated games and copymasters. This reduces the need for help with reading, but it is best to assume that many children will need questions to be read to them, as they go along.

Before children start work, talk to them about how important it is for them to do the best they can *on their own*, so that you and they can find out what things they still need to practise. Explain that although you would usually help them in maths, you would like them to try this sheet completely by themselves (although you *will* help with reading). Most children will feel more confident working in pencil not pen.

If a child is not successful with any part of the test then they should be given the opportunity to revise that area, and play any of the games which practise that concept (see *Games* on page 10). After a period of revision and practice give the child the alternative version of the test to record improvement.

The tests give a mark out of ten. The main items tested are:

Tests for Yellow Textbook 1

Question 1	Counting to 150
Question 2	Writing dates
Questions 3, 4 and 7	0, 1, 2, 3, 4, 5 and 10 times tables facts
Questions 5 and 6	Addition and subtraction within 80
Question 8	Finding $\frac{1}{2}$ and $\frac{1}{4}$ of numbers within 80
Questions 9 and 10	Multiplying by 2 or 3 within 80

Tests for Yellow Textbook 2

Question 1	Counting to 180
Question 2	Finding half of amounts of money within £10
Questions 3 and 4	3, 4, 5 and 10 times tables facts
Question 5	Finding missing numbers within 100
Question 6	Dividing by 2 within 100
Question 7	Reading a negative temperature
Question 8	Multiplying by 3 within 100
Questions 9 and 10	Addition and subtraction within 100

Tests for Yellow Textbook 3

Question 1	Counting to 200
Questions 2, 9 and 10	Addition and subtraction within 120
Questions 3 and 6	3, 4, 5 and 6 times tables facts
Questions 4 and 5	Recognising and counting in $\frac{1}{2}$s and $\frac{1}{4}$s
Question 7	Dividing by 3 within 80
Question 8	Multiplying by 3 or 4 within 120

Progress test

Yellow Textbook 1 Version A

Name _____

Date _____

1 This is 23.   How many is this? _____

2 Write each date the other way.

3rd September 1999 is _____

18/5/92 is _____

Write the missing numbers.

3 2 × 9 = _____

6 × 0 = _____

6 × 6 = _____

4 20 ÷ 5 = _____

27 ÷ 3 = _____

16 ÷ 4 = _____

5 I had 54p, then my mum gave me 12p.

How much have I got?

_____

6 I had 80p. I spent 63p.

How much is left?

_____

7 5 pies in a pack. How many pies in 6 packs? _____

5 APPLE PIES

8 What is $\frac{1}{2}$ of 64p? _____   What is $\frac{1}{4}$ of 64p? _____

9   26
     × 3
    _____

    _____

10   27
     × 2
    _____

    _____

Number Connections © Rose Griffiths 1997
Heinemann Educational Publishers, Oxford

Progress test

Yellow Textbook 1 Version B

Name _____

Date _____

1 This is 24.   How many is this? _____

 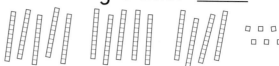

2 Write each date the other way.

2nd October 1998 is _____

19/4/93 is _____

Write the missing numbers.

3 $7 \times 0 =$ _____

  $3 \times 9 =$ _____

  $5 \times 5 =$ _____

4 $24 \div 3 =$ _____

  $20 \div 4 =$ _____

  $36 \div 6 =$ _____

5  I had 62p, then my dad gave me 15p.

How much have I got now?

_____

6 I had 80p. I spent 64p.

How much is left?

_____

7 5 pies in a pack. How many pies in 7 packs? _____

8 What is $\frac{1}{2}$ of 68p? _____   What is $\frac{1}{4}$ of 68p? _____

9   24
    $\times$ 3
    _____

    _____

10   28
    $\times$ 2
    _____

    _____

Progress test

Name _____

Date _____

1 This is 134.   How much is this? _____

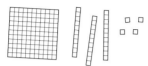 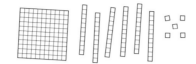

2 How much did these cost in the sale?

They are half price in the sale!

 £7·00

 £1·80

Write the missing numbers.

3 $10 \times 6 =$ _____

  $5 \times 8 =$ _____

4 $18 \div 3 =$ _____

  $28 \div 4 =$ _____

5 $29 + 40 =$ ☐

  $47 +$ ☐ $= 100$

6 $2 \overline{)\, 59}$

7

What is the temperature?

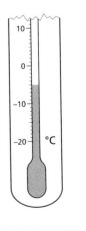

_____

8 27
   $\times\ 3$
   _____

   _____

9 32
   28
   $+ 36$
   _____

   _____

10 70
   $-\ 34$
   _____

   _____

Number Connections © Rose Griffiths 1997
Heinemann Educational Publishers, Oxford

Progress test

Yellow Textbook 2 Version B

Name _____

Date _____

1 This is 125.   How much is this? _____

   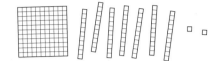

2 How much did these cost in the sale?

They are half price in the sale!

£9·00   £1·40

Write the missing numbers.

3 $7 \times 5 =$ _____

  $10 \times 9 =$ _____

4 $24 \div 4 =$ _____

  $27 \div 3 =$ _____

5 $27 + 50 =$ ▢

  $56 +$ ▢ $= 100$

6 $2 \overline{)\,57}$

7

What is the temperature?

_____

8   28
  × 3
  _____

  _____

9   34
  27
  + 26
  _____

  _____

10   70
  − 47
  _____

  _____

Progress test

Name _____

Date _____

1 This is 142.   How much is this? _____

 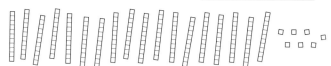

2

I've saved £19.
How much more do I need?

£35.

_____

3

I've saved £4 a month, for 7 months.
How much have I saved altogether?

_____

4 Write the missing numbers.

$\frac{1}{2}$, 1, $1\frac{1}{2}$, 2, _____, 3, _____, 4

5 Is each piece $\frac{1}{4}$? Write <u>Yes</u> or <u>No</u>.

 _____

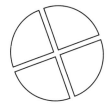 _____

6 $3 \times 9 =$ _____

$30 \div 6 =$ _____

7

$3\overline{)74}$

8 28
$\times\ 4$
_____

_____

9 19
$+\ 84$
_____

_____

10 90
$-\ 47$
_____

_____

Number Connections © Rose Griffiths 1997
Heinemann Educational Publishers, Oxford

Progress test

Name _____

Date _____

1 This is 136.   How much is this? _____

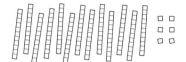 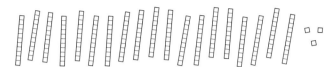

2

I've saved £17.
How much more do I need?

£34·

_____

3

I've saved £6 a month, for 6 months.
How much have I saved altogether?   _____

4 Write the missing numbers.

2, $2\frac{1}{2}$, 3, $3\frac{1}{2}$, 4, _____, 5, _____, 6

5 Is each piece $\frac{1}{4}$? Write <u>Yes</u> or <u>No</u>.

 _____

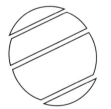 _____

6 $8 \times 4 =$ _____

   $24 \div 6 =$ _____

7

   $3 \overline{)\,77}$

8   37
   $\times\ 3$
   _____

   _____

9   24
   $+ 79$
   _____

   _____

10   90
   $- 46$
   _____

   _____

Number Connections © Rose Griffiths 1997
Heinemann Educational Publishers, Oxford

Record sheet

Pupil's name _____

Yellow Textbook 1

Mathematical content
▶ Counting to 150
▶ Using money
▶ Addition and subtraction within 80
▶ Mental recall of tables facts: all of the 0, 1, 2 and 10 times tables, *and* 3s, 4s and 5s within 25
▶ Ordinal numbers (1st to 31st)
▶ $\frac{1}{2}$s and $\frac{1}{4}$s
▶ Multiplying 2-digit numbers by 2 or 3 within 80

TEXTBOOK		Date completed	COPYMASTERS ✓ if used ✗ if not needed			Games (shade if played)
Page						
4 **Seeds and shells**	Counting to 150		Y1			
6 **Months and years**	Writing dates		Y2	Y3		
8 **Off by heart**	Mental recall of tables facts within 25		Y4			Times tables bingo
10 **Add or take away**	Add^n and sub^n within 80		Y5	Y6		
12 **Days and dates**	Understanding a calendar		Y7	Y8	Y9	
14 **Speedy tables**	Mental recall of tables facts		Y10			
16 **Squares**	Square numbers within 36		Y11	Y12		
18 **Ways of adding**	Addition within 80		Y13	Y14		Calculator race
20 **Times 2, times 3**	Multiplication within 80		Y15	Y16		
22 **Adding nine**	Addition of 9 within 80		Y17	Y18		
24 **More multiplying**	Multiplication within 80		Y19	Y20		
26 **Shopping**	Using money		Y21	Y22		
28 **Lunch**	Multipl^n and div^n by 2, 3, 4 and 5		Y23	Y24		
30 **Quarter each**	Finding a quarter of a group		Y25	Y26		
32 **Make forty**	Combinations to make 40					

Progress test	Date completed	Score out of 10
Version A		
Version B		

Other activities

Number Connections © Rose Griffiths 1997
Heinemann Educational Publishers, Oxford

Yellow Textbook 1	Name _____
Record sheet A	Date started _____

Page	Date completed	Copymasters		
4 Seeds and shells		Y1		
6 Months and years		Y2	Y3	
8 Off by heart		Y4		
10 Add or take away		Y5	Y6	
12 Days and dates		Y7	Y8	Y9
14 Speedy tables		Y10		
16 Squares		Y11	Y12	
18 Ways of adding		Y13	Y14	

Play from page 9 onwards

I played <u>Times tables bingo</u>
on _____ and _____

Play from page 19 onwards

I played <u>Calculator race</u>
on _____ and _____

Other activities

Number Connections © Rose Griffiths 1997
Heinemann Educational Publishers, Oxford

Yellow Textbook 1

Record sheet B

Name _____

Date started _____

Page		Date completed	Copymasters	
20	Times 2, times 3		Y15	Y16
22	Adding nine		Y17	Y18
24	More multiplying		Y19	Y20
26	Shopping		Y21	Y22
28	Lunch		Y23	Y24
30	Quarter each		Y25	Y26
32	Make forty			

I played <u>Times tables bingo</u>
on _____ and _____

I played <u>Calculator race</u>
on _____ and _____

Other activities

Number Connections © Rose Griffiths 1997
Heinemann Educational Publishers, Oxford

Record sheet

Pupil's name _____

Yellow Textbook 2

Mathematical content
- ▶ Counting to 180
- ▶ Using money
- ▶ Addition, subtraction and multiplication within 100
- ▶ Mental recall of tables facts: all of the 0, 1, 2, 3, 4, 5 and 10 times tables
- ▶ Multiples of 6 to 60
- ▶ Dividing 2-digit numbers by 2 within 100
- ▶ Negative numbers

TEXTBOOK		Date completed	COPYMASTERS ✓ if used ✗ if not needed			Games (shade if played)
4 **One hundred and eighty**	Counting to 180		Y31			
6 **How tall are you?**	Numbers in order, within 180		Y32	Y33		
8 **Half price sale**	Halving and doubling money		Y34	Y35	Half price sale	
10 **Tables stars**	Tables facts within 36		Y36	Y37		
12 **Ice pops**	Multiples of 5 and 10; negative numbers		Y38	Y39	Y40	
14 **More tables stars**	Tables facts within 36		Y41	Y42		
16 **Speedy tables**	Mental recall of tables facts		Y43			
18 **Keeping fit**	Add^n and sub^n within 100		Y44	Y45		
20 **Six times table**	Six times table		Y46	Y47		
22 **Multiplying**	Multiplication within 100		Y48	Y49		
24 **What's missing?**	Missing numbers and operations		Y50	Y51		What's missing?
26 **Dividing marbles**	Dividing by 2 within 100		Y52	Y53		
28 **More dividing**	Dividing by 2 within 100		Y54	Y55		
30 **Nines and tens**	Add^n and sub^n within 100		Y56	Y57		
32 **Make one hundred**	Addition to 100					

Progress test	Date completed	Score out of 10
Version A		
Version B		

Other activities

Number Connections © Rose Griffiths 1997
Heinemann Educational Publishers, Oxford

Yellow Textbook 2

Record sheet A

Name _____

Date started _____

Page	Date completed	Copymasters		
4 One hundred and eighty		Y31		
6 How tall are you?		Y32	Y33	
8 Half price sale		Y34	Y35	
10 Tables stars		Y36	Y37	
12 Ice pops		Y38	Y39	Y40
14 More tables stars		Y41	Y42	
16 Speedy tables		Y43		
18 Keeping fit		Y44	Y45	

Play from page 9 onwards

I played <u>Half price sale</u>
on _____ and _____

Other activities

Number Connections © Rose Griffiths 1997
Heinemann Educational Publishers, Oxford

Name _____

Date started _____

Page		Date completed	Copymasters	
20	Six times table		Y46	Y47
22	Multiplying		Y48	Y49
24	What's missing?		Y50	Y51
26	Dividing marbles		Y52	Y53
28	More dividing		Y54	Y55
30	Nines and tens		Y56	Y57
32	Make one hundred			

I played <u>Half price sale</u>
on _____ and _____

Play from page 25 onwards

I played <u>What's missing?</u>
on _____ and _____

Other activities

Record sheet

Yellow Textbook 3

Pupil's name _____

Mathematical content
► Counting to 200
► Using money
► Addition and subtraction within 120
► Mental recall of tables facts: all of the 0, 1, 2, 3, 4, 5 and 10 times tables, *and* 6s within 36
► Mental recall of number bonds within 20
► Multiplying and dividing by 2, 3, 5 and 10 within 120
► $\frac{1}{2}$s, $\frac{1}{4}$s, $\frac{1}{3}$s and $\frac{1}{5}$s

TEXTBOOK			COPYMASTERS		
Page		Date completed	✓ if used ✗ if not needed		Games (shade if played)
4 **Two hundred**	Counting to 200		Y63		
6 **Saving**	Using money		Y64	Y65	
8 **Teen sums**	Add^n bonds to 16, 17 and 18		Y66	Y67	Eighteens
10 **Halves**	Halving within 120		Y68	Y69	
12 **Speedy tables**	Mental recall of tables facts		Y70		
14 **Printing**	Multipl^n and div^n by 2 and 10		Y71	Y72	
16 **Sums to twenty**	Add^n and sub^n bonds within 20		Y73		Make 20
18 **Cheesecakes**	Comparing $\frac{1}{2}$s, $\frac{1}{3}$s, $\frac{1}{4}$s and $\frac{1}{5}$s		Y74	Y75	
20 **More printing**	Multipl^n and div^n by 3 within 120		Y76	Y77	
22 **Number cards**	Add^n and sub^n within 120		Y78	Y79	
24 **Guinea pig sums**	Arithmetic within 80		Y80	Y81	
26 **Inches and halves**	Using halves		Y82	Y83	
28 **Café**	Using money		Y84	Y85	
30 **Halves and quarters**	Using halves and quarters		Y86	Y87	
32 **Cubes in groups**	Divisibility by 2, 3, 4, 5 and 6				

Progress test	Date completed	Score out of 10
Version A		
Version B		

Other activities

Number Connections © Rose Griffiths 1997
Heinemann Educational Publishers, Oxford

Yellow Textbook 3

Record sheet A

Name _____

Date started _____

Page		Date completed	Copymasters	
4	Two hundred		Y63	
6	Saving		Y64	Y65
8	Teen sums		Y66	Y67
10	Halves		Y68	Y69
12	Speedy tables		Y70	
14	Printing		Y71	Y72
16	Sums to twenty		Y73	
18	Cheesecakes		Y74	Y75

Play from page 9 onwards

I played Eighteens
on _____ and _____

Play from page 17 onwards

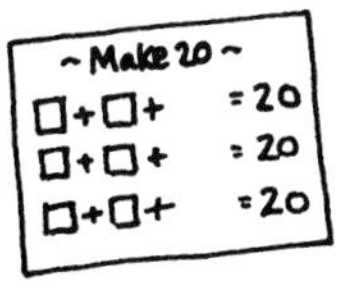

I played Make 20
on _____ and _____

Other activities

Number Connections © Rose Griffiths 1997
Heinemann Educational Publishers, Oxford

Yellow Textbook 3

Record sheet B

Name _____

Date started _____

Page		Date completed	Copymasters	
20	More printing		Y76	Y77
22	Number cards		Y78	Y79
24	Guinea pig sums		Y80	Y81
26	Inches and halves		Y82	Y83
28	Café		Y84	Y85
30	Halves and quarters		Y86	Y87
32	Cubes in groups			

I played <u>Eighteens</u>
on _____ and _____

I played <u>Make 20</u>
on _____ and _____

Other activities

Number Connections © Rose Griffiths 1997
Heinemann Educational Publishers, Oxford

Curriculum coverage charts: Yellow level

National Curriculum Key Stage 2 Programme of Study

Using and Applying Mathematics

'Using and Applying Mathematics' is integrated throughout *Number Connections*; every aspect of the programme of study is included.

Number		*Textbook 1*	*Textbook 2*	*Textbook 3*
1 Opportunities to:				
develop flexible and effective methods	a	■/▲	■/▲	▲
use calculators	b	■/▲	■/▲	■/▲
develop skills for use of equipment	c	■/▲	■/▲	▲
2 Developing an understanding of place value and extending the number system	a	■/▲	■/▲	■/▲
	b	■/▲	■/▲	■/▲
	c	■/▲	■/▲	■/▲
3 Understanding relationships between numbers and developing methods of computation	a	■/▲	■/▲	■/▲
	b			
	c	■/▲	■/▲	▲
	d	■/▲	■/▲	▲
	e	■/▲	■/▲	▲
	f	■/▲	■/▲	▲
	g	■/▲	■/▲	■/▲
	h	■/▲	■/▲	■/▲
4 Solving numerical problems	a	■/▲	■/▲	▲
	b	■/▲	■/▲	▲
	c	■/▲	■/▲	■/▲

● Level 1   ■ Level 2   ▲ Level 3

Mathematics 5 to 14 (Number, Money and Measurement)

Strand	*Textbook 1*	*Textbook 2*	*Textbook 3*
Range and type of numbers	■/▲	■/▲	■/▲
Money	■/▲	■/▲	■/▲
Add and subtract	■	■	■/▲
Multiply and divide	■	■	■/▲
Round numbers	■	■	■
Fractions, percentages and ratio	■	■	■
Patterns and sequences	■	■	■
Functions and equations	■	■	■

● Level A   ■ Level B   ▲ Level C

Northern Ireland Curriculum Key Stage 2 Programme of Study

Processes in Mathematics

'Processes in Mathematics' is integrated throughout
Number Connections; every aspect of the programme of study
relating to this attainment target is included.

Number		Textbook 1	Textbook 2	Textbook 3
Understanding number and number notation	a	■ /▲	■ /▲	▲
	b	■	■	■
	c	■ /▲	■ /▲	■ /▲
	d	■ /▲	■ /▲	■ /▲
Patterns, relationships and sequences	a	■ /▲	■ /▲	■ /▲
	b	■ /▲	■ /▲	■ /▲
	c	■	■	■
	d			
Operations and their application	a	■ /▲	■ /▲	■ /▲
	b	■ /▲	■ /▲	■ /▲
Money	a	■ /▲	■ /▲	■ /▲
	b	■ /▲	■ /▲	■ /▲
	c	■ /▲	■ /▲	■ /▲

● Level 1   ■ Level 2   ▲ Level 3